MOVIE PRODUCTION & BUDGET FORMS INSTANTLY!

Ralph S. Singleton

LONE
EAGLE

ACKNOWLEDGMENTS

Thank you to all the production managers, assistant directors, production coordinators, production accountants with whom I have worked over the years who, whether they realize it or not, have helped make this book possible.

A special thanks to Steve Goepel, Michael Kennedy, Jim Turner and Joan V. Singleton for their assistance in designing the budget form, to Gloriane Harris for her expert skills in the layout and paste-up of this book, and to Heidi Frieder for her terrific cover design and headline pages.

MOVIE PRODUCTION & BUDGET FORMS...INSTANTLY!

Copyright © 1985 Ralph S. Singleton

All rights reserved. Purchasers are authorized to reproduce for their own use without prior permission, or payment, provided that reproduction does not constitute republication of the book in whole or in part and that such reproductions are not offered for sale. Permission is not granted to store any of this information in any information or retrieval system.

LONE EAGLE PUBLISHING COMPANY
2337 Roscomare Road, Suite Nine
Los Angeles, CA 90077
310/471-8066
1/800-FILMBKS
FAX 310/471-4969

Printed in the United States of America

Cover designed by Heidi Frieder

Typesetting by Communigraphics, Inc., Los Angeles, CA

ISBN 0-943728-14-2

10 9 8 7

TABLE OF CONTENTS

INTRODUCTION

Movie Production & Budget Forms. . .Instantly! has been designed with the independent producer in mind. All forms are 8½" x 11" when photocopied so they will fit inside your three-ring project binder, file folders, briefcases, etc. By positioning these forms correctly on your copier, you will eliminate our page numbers and book title and will get clean, readable forms. All the forms are perforated so they can be removed easily and be used again and again.

BUDGET FORM

Those of you who have already read **Film Scheduling, Film Budgeting** and the **Film Scheduling/Film Budgeting Workbook** should be familiar with the forms. The budget form is the most complete one available at this writing. (A): Fringeable/Taxable: is for all Union Labor; (B): Non-Fringeable/Taxable is for all non-Union or non-fringeable labor; and (C): Non-Fringeable/Non-Taxable is usually for all material costs (with the exception of sales tax). You should find these categories very helpful when preparing your budget.

PRODUCTION FORMS

Prior to this, most production forms were hand-me-downs of forms used on a previous production. Sometimes some changes were made, oftentimes not. What resulted was a hodge-podge of forms which lacked detail, continuity and were extremely outdated. Some hadn't been changed in over thirty years! The production forms included here have all been redesigned and integrated. We think you will find them much easier to work with on your next production.

NOT JUST FOR 35 MM

Although the thrust of this book is for professional 35mm feature productions, these forms can easily be adapted to 16mm, 8mm and video productions. The Second Unit section is so complete that many short film and commercial productions are using that section alone as their complete budget.

With **Movie Production & Budget Forms. . .Instantly!** you will always have the forms you need, when you need them. No more bulky legal size forms that won't fit in briefcases and notebooks! No more having to buy a whole pad of a single form when all you need is one! No more having to create your own forms, or postpone budgeting a project because you don't have a budget form.

I welcome your comments about these forms. As this book will be revised from time to time, let me know what other forms you would like included. Send your comments to me in care of my publisher. The address is on the copyright page.

Good luck with your project.

Ralph S. Singleton
Beverly Hills
April 1985

BUDGET FORM

Budget Form

FILM PRODUCTION BUDGET

DATE: _____

PRODUCTION COMPANY	PRODUCTION TITLE	PRODUCTION NO.
EXECUTIVE PRODUCER	PRODUCER	DIRECTOR	PRODUCTION MANAGER
START DATE	FINISH DATE	SCRIPT DATED	SCRIPT PAGES	CREW DAILY PAY HRS.

ACCT NO.	DESCRIPTION	PAGE NO.	BUDGET	TOTALS
0000	Development	3		
1000	Story and Screenplay	4		
1100	Producers Unit	5		
1200	Directors Unit	6		
1300	Cast Unit	7		
1400	Travel and Living	8		
1900	Fringe Benefits and Payroll Taxes	9		
	TOTAL ABOVE THE LINE			
2000	Production Department	10		
2100	Extra Talent	11		
2200	Art Department	12		
2300	Set Construction	13		
2400	Set Dressing	14		
2500	Property	15		
2600	Picture Vehicles	16		
2700	Special Effects	17		
2800	Camera	18		
3000	Special Equipment	19		
3100	Sound	20		
3200	Grip	21		
3300	Lighting	22		
3400	Wardrobe	23		
3500	Makeup and Hair	24		
3600	Set Operations	25, 26		
3700	Site Rental	27		
3800	Stage Rental and Expense	28		
4000	Location Expense	29, 30		
4100	Second Unit	31, 32		
4200	Tests	33		
4300	Miniatures	34		
4400	Process	35		
4500	Animals	36		
4600	Transportation	37		
4700	Raw Stock and Laboratory	38		
4900	Fringe Benefits and Payroll Taxes	39		
	TOTAL BELOW THE LINE			

©1984 Lone Eagle Productions, Inc.

FILM PRODUCTION BUDGET (Cont'd)

DATE: _____

PRODUCTION COMPANY _____   PRODUCTION TITLE _____   PRODUCTION NO. _____

ACCT NO.	DESCRIPTION	PAGE NO.	BUDGET	TOTALS
5000	Film Editing	40, 41		
5100	Music	42		
5200	Film Effects	43		
5300	Titles	44		
5400	Post Production Sound	45		
5500	Post Production Film	46		
5900	Fringe Benefits and Payroll Taxes	47		
	TOTAL POST PRODUCTION			
6000	Publicity	48		
6100	Insurance	49		
6200	General Expense	50		
6900	Fringe Benefits and Payroll Taxes	51		
	TOTAL OTHER COSTS			
	TOTAL DIRECT COSTS			
7500	Contingency	52		
7600	Completion Bond	52		
7700	Overhead	52		
7800	Interest	52		
	TOTAL NEGATIVE COSTS			
8000	Deferments	52		
	TOTAL NEGATIVE COSTS (Incl. Deferments)			

PRODUCTION DAYS

Rehearsal	
Studio	
Loc. Location	
Distant Location	
Holidays	
Travel	
Total Production Days	

BUDGET APPROVALS

_____   _____
Estimator   Exec. in Charge of Prod.

_____   _____
Producer   Production Manager

_____
Date

© 1984 Lone Eagle Productions, Inc.

PROD. NO. _____   PROD. TITLE _____   DATE:_____

0000	DEVELOPMENT COSTS	SUBTOTALS		
ACCT. NO.	DESCRIPTION	A	B	C
	Story and Screenplay			
	Rights and Options			
	Drafts and Treatments			
	Typing			
	Script Duplication			
	Producer's Unit			
	Producer			
	Assoc. Producer			
	Secretary			
	Additional Hire			
	Director's Unit			
	Director			
	Secretary			
	Additional Hire			
	Budget Preparation			
	Script Breakdown, Production Board and			
	Budget Preparation Fee			
	Accounting			
	Legal			
	Incorporation			
	Contracts			
	Business License			
	Other			
	Office Overhead			
	Telephone and Telex			
	Answering Service			
	Telephone Installation Charge			
	Office Rent			
	Equipment/Furniture			
	Rental			
	Purchase			
	Data Processing			
	Supplies			
	Stationery			
	Postage			
	Transportation			
	Car Allowance			
	Gas, Oil			
	Additional Expenses			
	Miscellaneous			
	Fringe Benefits			
	SUBTOTALS			
	TOTAL ACCT 0000			

A - Fringeable/Taxable
B - Non-Fringeable/Taxable
C - Non-Taxable

PROD. NO. _____   PROD. TITLE _____   DATE:_____

1000   STORY AND SCREENPLAY

ACCT. NO.	DESCRIPTION	LOCAL/ ON LOC.	DAYS/WEEKS				RATE	SUBTOTALS		
			PREP	SHOOT	WRAP	TOTAL		A	B	C
10	Rights & Expenses	Local								
		On Loc.								
		Local								
		On Loc.								
20	Writers	Local								
		On Loc.								
		Local								
		On Loc.								
30	Script Writing	Local								
		On Loc.								
		Local								
		On Loc.								
40	Script Duplication	Local								
		On Loc.								
		Local								
		On Loc.								
50	Script Timing	Local								
		On Loc.								
		Local								
		On Loc.								
60	Secretary(ies)	Local								
		On Loc.								
		Local								
		On Loc.								
		Local								
		On Loc.								
70	Research, Technical, Screenings									
85	Additional Expenses									
95	Miscellaneous									
						SUBTOTALS				
					TOTAL ACCT 1000					

A - Fringeable/Taxable
B - Non-Fringeable/Taxable
C - Non-Taxable

PROD. NO. _____　PROD. TITLE _____　DATE:_____

1100　PRODUCERS UNIT

ACCT. NO.	DESCRIPTION	LOCAL/ ON LOC.	DAYS/WEEKS				RATE	SUBTOTALS		
			PREP	SHOOT	WRAP	TOTAL		A	B	C
01	Executive Producer(s)	Local								
		On Loc.								
		Local								
		On Loc.								
02	Producer(s)	Local								
		On Loc.								
		Local								
		On Loc.								
03	Associate Producer(s)	Local								
		On Loc.								
		Local								
		On Loc.								
60	Secretary(ies)	Local								
		On Loc.								
		Local								
		On Loc.								
		Local								
		On Loc.								
		Local								
		On Loc.								
		Local								
		On Loc.								
		Local								
		On Loc.								
70	Research, Technical, Screenings									
80	Packaging Fee									
85	Additional Expenses									
95	Miscellaneous									
99	Loss, Damage, Repair									
							SUBTOTALS			
						TOTAL ACCT 1100				

A - Fringeable/Taxable
B - Non-Fringeable/Taxable
C - Non-Taxable

PROD. NO. _____   PROD. TITLE _____   DATE:_____

1200   DIRECTORS UNIT

ACCT. NO.	DESCRIPTION	LOCAL/ ON LOC.	DAYS/WEEKS				RATE	SUBTOTALS		
			PREP	SHOOT	WRAP	TOTAL		A	B	C
01	Director	Local								
		On Loc.								
		Local								
		On Loc.								
02	Second Unit Director	Local								
		On Loc.								
		Local								
		On Loc.								
03	Choreographer	Local								
		On Loc.								
		Local								
		On Loc.								
04	Dialogue Director	Local								
		On Loc.								
		Local								
		On Loc.								
60	Secretary(ies)	Local								
		On Loc.								
		Local								
		On Loc.								
		Local								
		On Loc.								
		Local								
		On Loc.								
70	Research, Technical, Screenings									
85	Additional Expenses									
95	Miscellaneous									
							SUBTOTALS			
							TOTAL ACCT 1200			

A - Fringeable/Taxable
B - Non-Fringeable/Taxable
C - Non-Taxable

PROD. NO. _____   PROD. TITLE _____   DATE:_____

1300 CAST UNIT					SUBTOTALS		
ACCT. NO.	DESCRIPTION	TIME	RATE	AMOUNT	A	B	C
01	Principal Players						
	(See Detail Page 7A)						
02	Supporting Players						
	(See Detail Page 7B)						
03	Day Players						
	(See Detail Page 7C)						
04	Stunt Coordinator						
05	Stunts (See Detail Page 7D)						
06	Looping						
07	Overtime						
08	Cast Expenses						
09	Casting Expenses						
10	Welfare Worker/Teacher						
11	Rehearsal Expenses						
85	Additional Expenses						
95	Miscellaneous						
				SUBTOTALS			
				TOTAL ACCT 1300			

A - Fringeable/Taxable
B - Non-Fringeable/Taxable
C - Non-Taxable

PROD. NO. _____　PROD. TITLE _____　DATE:_____

1301　PRINCIPAL PLAYERS

| CAST NO. | CHARACTER | DAYS/WEEKS | | | RATE | SUBTOTALS | | |
		WORK	HOLD	TOTAL		A	B	C
					SUBTOTALS			
			TOTAL DETAIL ACCT 1301					

A - Fringeable/Taxable
B - Non-Fringeable/Taxable
C - Non-Taxable

PROD. NO. _____ PROD. TITLE _____ DATE:_____

1302 SUPPORTING PLAYERS

CAST NO.	CHARACTER	DAYS/WEEKS			RATE	SUBTOTALS		
		WORK	HOLD	TOTAL		A	B	C
		SUBTOTALS						
		TOTAL DETAIL ACCT 1302						

A - Fringeable/Taxable   C - Non-Taxable
B - Non-Fringeable/Taxable

PROD. NO. _____ PROD. TITLE _____ DATE:_____

1303	DAY PLAYERS						SUBTOTALS		
CAST NO.	CHARACTER	DAYS			RATE	A	B	C
		WORK	HOLD	TOTAL				
					SUBTOTALS			
					TOTAL DETAIL ACCT 1303			

A - Fringeable/Taxable   C - Non-Taxable
B - Non-Fringeable/Taxable

©1984 Lone Eagle Productions, Inc.

PROD. NO. _____   PROD. TITLE _____   DATE:_____

1305   STUNTS

| CAST NO. | SCENE DESCRIPTION/NOS. | DAYS/WEEKS | | | RATE | SUBTOTALS | | |
		WORK	HOLD	TOTAL		A	B	C
		SUBTOTALS						
		TOTAL DETAIL ACCT 1305						

A - Fringeable/Taxable   C - Non-Taxable
B - Non-Fringeable/Taxable

LOCATION EXPENSE—DETAIL

PROD. NO. _____   PROD. TITLE _____   DATE: _____

1400 TRAVEL AND LIVING—ABOVE-THE-LINE

POSITION/NAME	DESTINATION (RT)	AIRFARES			LODGING (PER DIEM)			MEALS (PER DIEM)				TOTALS
		NO. FLIGHTS	RATE	SUBTOTAL	NO. DAYS	RATE	SUBTOTAL	NO. DAYS		RATE	SUBTOTAL	
									B			
									L			
									D			
									B			
									L			
									D			
									B			
									L			
									D			
									B			
									L			
									D			
									B			
									L			
									D			
									B			
									L			
									D			
									B			
									L			
									D			
									B			
									L			
									D			
SUBTOTALS		1401			1402			1403				

TOTAL DETAIL ACCT 1400

A - Fringeable/Taxable
B - Non-Fringeable/Taxable
C - Non-Taxable

©1984 Lone Eagle Productions, Inc.

PROD. NO. _____ PROD. TITLE _____ DATE:_____

1900 FRINGE BENEFITS AND PAYROLL TAXES—ABOVE-THE-LINE

ACCT NO.	DESCRIPTION	PAYROLL	PENSION	HEALTH & WELFARE	TOTALS
01	DGA $ _____	% _____	% _____	% _____	
02	PGA $ _____	% _____	% _____	% _____	
03	WGA $ _____	% _____	% _____	% _____	
04	SAG $ _____	% _____	% _____	% _____	
05	IATSE $ _____	% _____	% _____	% _____	
06	NABET $ _____	% _____	% _____	% _____	
07	OTHER $ _____	% _____	% _____	% _____	
10	or Allow				

SUBTOTALS [ ] [ ] [ ] [ ]

TOTAL ACCT 1900 [ ]

TOTAL COST ABOVE-THE-LINE [ ]

PROD. NO. _____   PROD. TITLE _____   DATE:_____

2000 PRODUCTION DEPARTMENT

NO.	DESCRIPTION	LOCAL/ ON LOC.	DAYS/WEEKS				RATE	SUBTOTALS		
			PREP	SHOOT	WRAP	TOTAL		A	B	C
01	Production Manager	Local								
		On Loc.								
		Local								
		On Loc.								
02	First Assistant Director	Local								
		On Loc.								
		Local								
		On Loc.								
03	Second Assistant Director	Local								
		On Loc.								
		Local								
		On Loc.								
05	Location Manager	Local								
		On Loc.								
		Local								
		On Loc.								
10	Production Accountant	Local								
		On Loc.								
15	Asst. to Production Accountant	Local								
		On Loc.								
20	D.G.A. Trainee	Local								
		On Loc.								
25	Production Assts.	Local								
		On Loc.								
		Local								
		On Loc.								
48	Interpreters	Local								
		On Loc.								
50	Script Supervisor	Local								
		On Loc.								
55	Production Office Coordinator	Local								
		On Loc.								
60	Production Secretary	Local								
		On Loc.								
	Additional Hire	Local								
		On Loc.								
80	Technical Advisor	Local								
		On Loc.								
85	Additional Expenses									
95	Miscellaneous									
97	Production Board/ Budget Prep.									
						SUBTOTALS				
				TOTAL ACCT 2000						

A - Fringeable/Taxable   C - Non-Taxable
B - Non-Fringeable/Taxable

©1984 Lone Eagle Productions, Inc.

PROD. NO. _____ PROD. TITLE _____ DATE: _____

| 2100 | EXTRA TALENT | | | | SUBTOTALS | | |
ACCT. NO.	DESCRIPTION	TIME	RATE	AMT.	A	B	C
01	Extra Casting Fee						
03	Payroll Fee						
05	Extra Casting Expenses						
10	Welfare Workers/Teachers						
20	Extras & Stand-ins						
	(Detail Following Page 11A)						
35	Dancers/Swimmers						
43	Music Contractor						
45	Sideline Musicians						
48	Interviews/Fittings						
60	Extras Mileage Allowance (See Detail Page 11A)						
	Buses (See Transportation Acct 4603)						
	Meals (See Catering Acct 3620)						
70	Rehearsal Expenses						
	Additional Hire						
85	Additional Expenses						
95	Miscellaneous						
99	Loss, Damage, Repair						
				SUBTOTALS			
			TOTAL ACCT 2100				

A - Fringeable/Taxable   C - Non-Taxable
B - Non-Fringeable/Taxable

©1984 Lone Eagle Productions, Inc.

2100 EXTRA TALENT—DETAIL

DAY NO.	BREAK-DOWN PAGE	SCENE NO.	SCENE NAME/DESCRIPTION	A—GENERAL B—STAND-INS			C—SILENT BITS D—SPECIAL EXTRAS			O.T. ADJ.	MILEAGE			SUBTOTALS	
				NO.	RATE	AMOUNT	NO.	RATE	AMOUNT		NO.	RATE	AMOUNT	A	B
											SUBTOTALS				
										TOTAL DETAIL ACCT 2100					

A - Fringeable/Taxable
B - Non-Fringeable/Taxable
C - Non-Taxable

©1984 Lone Eagle Productions, Inc.

PROD. NO. _____ PROD. TITLE _____ DATE:_____

2200 ART DEPARTMENT

ACCT. NO.	DESCRIPTION	LOCAL/ ON LOC.	DAYS/WEEKS				RATE	SUBTOTALS		
			PREP	SHOOT	WRAP	TOTAL		A	B	C
01	Production Designer	Local								
		On Loc.								
02	Art Director	Local								
		On Loc.								
03	Assistant Art Director	Local								
		On Loc.								
04	Set Designer	Local								
		On Loc.								
		Local								
		On Loc.								
05	Draftsman	Local								
		On Loc.								
		Local								
		On Loc.								
09	Sketch Artist	Local								
		On Loc.								
10	Set Model Builders	Local								
		On Loc.								
15	Set Estimator	Local								
		On Loc.								
	Additional Hire	Local								
		On Loc.								
		Local								
		On Loc.								
		Local								
		On Loc.								
30	Rentals									
40	Purchases									
70	Research									
85	Additional Expense									
95	Miscellaneous									
99	Loss, Damage, Repair									
						SUBTOTALS				
						TOTAL ACCT 2200				

A - Fringeable/Taxable
B - Non-Fringeable/Taxable
C - Non-Taxable

PROD. NO. _____ PROD. TITLE _____ DATE:_____

2300 SET CONSTRUCTION

ACCT. NO.	DESCRIPTION		LOCAL/ ON LOC.	PREP	SHOOT	WRAP	TOTAL	RATE	A	B	C
					DAYS/WEEKS				SUBTOTALS		
01	Construction Coordinator		Local								
			On Loc.								
05	Construction Foreman		Local								
			On Loc.								
	Labor	NO.									
11	Painters		Local								
			On Loc.								
12	Scenic Artists		Local								
			On Loc.								
13	Carpenters		Local								
			On Loc.								
14	Propmakers		Local								
			On Loc.								
15	Laborers		Local								
			On Loc.								
16	Plumbers		Local								
			On Loc.								
17	Electrical Fixtures Man		Local								
			On Loc.								
18	Plasterers		Local								
			On Loc.								
			Local								
			On Loc.								
	Additional Hire		Local								
			On Loc.								
20	Set Construction Materials (See 13A)										
30	Set Equipment/Rentals (See 13B)										
35	Backings (See 13A)										
40	Set Equipment/Purchases (See 13B)										
55	Set Striking Maintenance (See 13A)										
	Rigging (See 13A)										
	Greens (See Set Dressing Acct 2410)										
75	Pickup and Delivery										
85	Additional Expense										
95	Miscellaneous										
99	Loss, Damage, Repair										
							SUBTOTALS				
							TOTAL ACCT 2300				

A - Fringeable/Taxable
B - Non-Fringeable/Taxable
C - Non-Taxable

©1984 Lone Eagle Productions, Inc.

PROD. NO. _____ PROD. TITLE _____ DATE:_____

2300 SET CONSTRUCTION DETAIL   SUBTOTALS

SET NO.	SCENE NAME/NO. DESCRIPTION	LABOR	MATERIALS	BACKINGS	SET RIGGING	SET STRIKING	A	B	C
								SUBTOTALS		
							TOTAL DETAIL ACCT 2300		

A - Fringeable/Taxable
B - Non-Fringeable/Taxable
C - Non-Taxable

2400 SET DRESSING

ACCT. NO.	DESCRIPTION	LOCAL/ ON LOC.	DAYS/WEEKS				RATE	SUBTOTALS		
			PREP	SHOOT	WRAP	TOTAL		A	B	C
01	Set Decorator	Local								
		On Loc.								
05	Swing Gang— Leadman	Local								
		On Loc.								
06	Swing Gang— Second	Local								
		On Loc.								
07	Swing Gang— Local	Local								
		On Loc.								
10	Greensman	Local								
		On Loc.								
12	Draperer	Local								
		On Loc.								
15	Standby Painter	Local								
		On Loc.								
	Additional Hire	Local								
		On Loc.								
		Local								
		On Loc.								
20	Set Dressing Manufactured—Labor									
25	Drapery and Upholstery—Labor									
30	Rentals									
	Set Dressing (See Detail Page 14A)									
	Paint Box									
	Greens									
40	Purchases									
	Set Dressing (See Detail Page 14A)									
	Expendables									
	Paint									
	Greens									
75	Delivery and Pickup Charges									
85	Additional Expense									
95	Miscellaneous									
99	Loss, Damage, Repair									
					SUBTOTALS					
					TOTAL ACCT 2400					

A - Fringeable/Taxable
B - Non-Fringeable/Taxable
C - Non-Taxable

©1984 Lone Eagle Productions, Inc.

PROD. NO. _____ PROD. TITLE _____ DATE:_____

ACCTS 2430 & 2440   SET DRESSING—DETAIL

SET NO.	SCENE NAME/NO. DESCRIPTION	QTY	ITEM DESCRIPTION	RENTALS TIME	RATE	AMOUNT	PURCHASES AMOUNT	✔
				SUBTOTALS				
			TOTAL DETAIL ACCTS 2430 & 2440				

A - Fringeable/Taxable   C - Non-Taxable
B - Non-Fringeable/Taxable   ✔ - Recoupable

©1984 Lone Eagle Productions, Inc.

PROD. NO. _____   PROD. TITLE _____   DATE:_____

2500   PROP DEPARTMENT

ACCT. NO.	DESCRIPTION	LOCAL/ ON LOC.	DAYS/WEEKS				RATE	SUBTOTALS		
			PREP	SHOOT	WRAP	TOTAL		A	B	C
01	Propmaster	Local								
		On Loc.								
		Local								
		On Loc.								
02	Asst. Propmaster	Local								
		On Loc.								
		Local								
		On Loc.								
03	Add'l. Asst. Propmaster	Local								
		On Loc.								
		Local								
		On Loc.								
		Local								
		On Loc.								
	Additional Hire	Local								
		On Loc.								
		Local								
		On Loc.								
		Local								
		On Loc.								
		Local								
		On Loc.								
		Local								
		On Loc.								
		Local								
		On Loc.								
30	Prop Rentals (See Detail Page 15A)									
	Video Playback System									
	Prop Box									
40	Prop Purchases (See Detail Page 15A)									
50	Props Manufactured—Labor									
55	Props Manufactured—Materials									
65	Permits (Guns and Ammo.)									
75	Pickup and Delivery									
85	Additional Expense									
95	Miscellaneous									
99	Loss, Damage, Repair									
						SUBTOTALS				
					TOTAL ACCT 2500					

A - Fringeable/Taxable
B - Non-Fringeable/Taxable
C - Non-Taxable

©1984 Lone Eagle Productions, Inc.

PROD. NO. _____   PROD. TITLE _____   DATE:_____

ACCTS 2530 & 2540 PROPS—DETAIL

SET NO.	SCENE NAME/NO. DESCRIPTION	QTY	ITEM DESCRIPTION	RENTALS			PURCHASES	✔
				TIME	RATE	AMOUNT	AMOUNT	
				SUBTOTALS				
			TOTAL DETAIL ACCTS 2530 & 2540				

A - Fringeable/Taxable   C - Non-Taxable
B - Non-Fringeable/Taxable   ✔ - Recoupable

PROD. NO. _____ PROD. TITLE _____ DATE: _____

2600 PICTURE VEHICLES	SUBTOTALS		
ACCT. NO. / DESCRIPTION	A	B	C
01 Vehicle Drivers (Non-Teamsters/Vehicle's owner or representative)			
02			
Transportation Allowance (See Location Acct 4005)			
30 Rental (See Detail Page 16A)			
Cars/Trucks			
Motorcycles			
Planes/Helicopters			
Trains			
Boats			
40 Purchases (See Detail Page 16A)			
Cars/Trucks			
Motorcycles			
Planes/Helicopters			
Trains			
Boats			
Car Carrier (See Transportation Acct No. 4600)			
45 Special Vehicle Use Permit (Check local regulations)			
48 Vehicle Alterations, Modifications, and Repairs			
Gas and Oil (See Transportation Acct 4650)			
60 Permits, Parking, Tolls, Fees, etc. (See Transportation Acct 4669)			
65 Rigging Maintenance			
70 Storage			
72 Security			
75 Shop			
Insurance (See Insurance Acct No. 6100)			
85 Additional Expenses			
95 Miscellaneous			
99 Loss, Damage, Repair			
SUBTOTALS			
TOTAL ACCT 2600			

A - Fringeable/Taxable C - Non-Taxable
B - Non-Fringeable/Taxable ©1984 Lone Eagle Productions, Inc.

PROD. NO. _____ PROD. TITLE _____ DATE:_____

ACCTS 2630 & 2640 PICTURE VEHICLES—DETAIL

SET NO.	SCENE NAME/NO. DESCRIPTION	QTY	VEHICLES DESCRIPTION	RENTAL TIME	RATE	AMOUNT	PURCHASES AMOUNT	✔
				SUBTOTALS				
			TOTAL DETAIL ACCTS 2630 & 2640				

A - Fringeable/Taxable   C - Non-Taxable
B - Non-Fringeable/Taxable   ✔ - Recoupable

©1984 Lone Eagle Productions, Inc.

PROD. NO. _____   PROD. TITLE _____   DATE:_____

2700 SPECIAL EFFECTS DEPARTMENT

ACCT. NO.	DESCRIPTION	LOCAL/ ON LOC.	DAYS/WEEKS				RATE	SUBTOTALS		
			PREP	SHOOT	WRAP	TOTAL		A	B	C
01	Special Effects Foreman	Local								
		On Loc.								
		Local								
		On Loc.								
02	Assistant Spec. Eff. Men	Local								
		On Loc.								
		Local								
		On Loc.								
	Additional Hire	Local								
		On Loc.								
		Local								
		On Loc.								
05	Rigging	Local								
		On Loc.								
		Local								
		On Loc.								
06	Striking	Local								
		On Loc.								
30	Equipment Rentals									
	Wind									
	Rain									
	Snow									
	Fog									
	Fire Hose Wet Downs									
	Box Rental (Water Wagon—See Transportation Acct 4630)									
40	Equipment Purchases									
	Explosives, Breakaways, etc.									
50	Manufacturing—Labor									
55	Manufacturing—Materials									
65	Permits (Explosives, Fire, etc.)									
79	Other Charges, Permits, Fees, etc.									
85	Additional Expense									
95	Miscellaneous									
99	Loss, Damage, Repair									
						SUBTOTALS				
						TOTAL ACCT 2700				

A - Fringeable/Taxable
B - Non-Fringeable/Taxable
C - Non-Taxable

PROD. NO. _____ PROD. TITLE _____ DATE:_____

ACCTS 2730 & 2740 SPECIAL EFFECTS—DETAIL

SET NO.	SCENE NAME/NO. DESCRIPTION	QTY	ITEM DESCRIPTION	RENTALS TIME	RATE	AMOUNT	PURCHASES AMOUNT	✔

SUBTOTALS		
TOTAL DETAIL ACCTS 2730 & 2740		

A - Fringeable/Taxable   C - Non-Taxable
B - Non-Fringeable/Taxable   ✔ - Recoupable

©1984 Lone Eagle Productions, Inc.

PROD. NO. _____   PROD. TITLE _____   DATE:_____

2800   CAMERA DEPARTMENT

ACCT. NO.	DESCRIPTION	LOCAL/ ON LOC.	DAYS/WEEKS				RATE	SUBTOTALS		
			PREP	SHOOT	WRAP	TOTAL		A	B	C
01	Director of Photography	Local								
		On Loc.								
		Local								
		On Loc.								
		Local								
		On Loc.								
02	Camera Operator	Local								
		On Loc.								
03	Additional Camera Operator	Local								
		On Loc.								
		Local								
		On Loc.								
05	1st Assistant Cameraman	Local								
		On Loc.								
		Local								
		On Loc.								
10	2nd Assistant Cameraman	Local								
		On Loc.								
12	Add'l 2nd Ass't Cameraman	Local								
		On Loc.								
	Still Photographer (See Publicity, Acct 6000)	Local								
		On Loc.								
15	Special Camera Operator	Local								
		On Loc.								
	Additional Hire	Local								
		On Loc.								
30	Rentals									
	First Camera System									
	Second Camera System									
	Through-The-Lens Video System									
	Other									
40	Purchases									
85	Additional Expense									
95	Miscellaneous									
99	Loss, Damage, Repair									
						SUBTOTALS				
						TOTAL ACCT 2800				

A - Fringeable/Taxable
B - Non-Fringeable/Taxable
C - Non-Taxable

PROD. NO. _____ PROD. TITLE _____ DATE:_____

3000	SPECIAL EQUIPMENT							
ACCT NO.	DESCRIPTION / SCENE NO.	RENTAL	PURCHASE	LABOR	FUEL/ MATERIALS	PICK-UP DELIVERY	OTHER	TOTAL
01	Helicopter							
05	Plane							
10	Train							
15	Boat							
20	Underwater Equipment							
25	Industrial Crane							
31	Scissors Lift							
35	Cherry Picker							
	Hand Held Camera							
	(See Camera Dept. Acct 2800)							
42	Wind Machine							
45	Low Boy							
	Additional Equipment							

					SUBTOTAL		
		TIME	RATE	AMOUNT	SUBTOTALS		
					A	B	C
	Per Diem (List on Page 30C)						
	Travel (List on Page 30C)						
85	Additional Expenses						
95	Miscellaneous						
99	Loss, Damage, Repair						
	SUBTOTALS						
	TOTAL ACCT 3000						

A - Fringeable/Taxable
B - Non-Fringeable/Taxable
C - Non-Taxable

©1984 Lone Eagle Productions, Inc.

PROD. NO. _____ PROD. TITLE _____ DATE:_____

3100 SOUND DEPARTMENT

ACCT. NO.	DESCRIPTION	LOCAL/ ON LOC.	DAYS/WEEKS				RATE	SUBTOTALS		
			PREP	SHOOT	WRAP	TOTAL		A	B	C
01	Mixer	Local								
		On Loc.								
		Local								
		On Loc.								
02	Mike Boom Operator	Local								
		On Loc.								
		Local								
		On Loc.								
03	Cable Puller	Local								
		On Loc.								
		Local								
		On Loc.								
04	Playback Operator	Local								
		On Loc.								
		Local								
		On Loc.								
05	P.A. Operator	Local								
		On Loc.								
		Local								
		On Loc.								
	Additional Hire	Local								
		On Loc.								
		Local								
		On Loc.								
06	Daily Transfers (Labor)	Local								
		On Loc.								
30	Equipment Rentals									
	Basic Sound Package									
	Radio Mikes									
	Walkie-Talkies									
	Playback									
	P.A.									
	Special Boom									
	Bullhorn									
40	Equipment Purchases									
	1/4" Audiotape—Batteries (See Prod. Rawstock Acct. 4700)									
85	Additional Expense									
95	Miscellaneous									
99	Loss, Damage, Repair									
						SUBTOTALS				
					TOTAL ACCT 3100					

A - Fringeable/Taxable
B - Non-Fringeable/Taxable
C - Non-Taxable

PROD. NO. _____ PROD. TITLE _____ DATE:_____

3200 GRIP DEPARTMENT

ACCT. NO.	DESCRIPTION	LOCAL/ ON LOC.	DAYS/WEEKS				RATE	SUBTOTALS		
			PREP	SHOOT	WRAP	TOTAL		A	B	C
01	Key Grip	Local								
		On Loc.								
		Local								
		On Loc.								
02	2nd Company Grip	Local								
		On Loc.								
		Local								
		On Loc.								
03	Dolly Grip	Local								
		On Loc.								
04	Crane Grip	Local								
		On Loc.								
05	Company Grip	Local								
		On Loc.								
		Local								
		On Loc.								
		Local								
		On Loc.								
	Additional Hire	Local								
		On Loc.								
		Local								
		On Loc.								
06	Rigging & Striking (See Also Acct 2300)	Local								
		On Loc.								
		Local								
		On Loc.								
30	Rentals									
	Dolly									
	Dolly Track									
	Crane									
	Grip Package									
40	Purchases									
	Gels									
85	Additional Expense									
95	Miscellaneous									
99	Loss, Damage, Repair									
						SUBTOTALS				
						TOTAL ACCT 3200				

A - Fringeable/Taxable
B - Non-Fringeable/Taxable
C - Non-Taxable

PROD. NO. _____   PROD. TITLE _____   DATE: _____

3300 LIGHTING DEPARTMENT

ACCT. NO.	DESCRIPTION	LOCAL/ ON LOC.	DAYS/WEEKS				RATE	SUBTOTALS		
			PREP	SHOOT	WRAP	TOTAL		A	B	C
01	Gaffer	Local								
		On Loc.								
03	Best Boy	Local								
		On Loc.								
04	Generator Operator	Local								
		On Loc.								
05	Electricians	Local								
		On Loc.								
	Additional Hire	Local								
		On Loc.								
		Local								
		On Loc.								
06	Rigging & Striking (See Also Acct 2300)	Local								
		On Loc.								
		Local								
		On Loc.								
		Local								
		On Loc.								
30	Equipment Rentals									
	Generator (A.C./D.C. Power)									
	Equipment Package									
	Lamps, Arc Lights (D.C. Power)									
	Dimmers/Cables, Connectors									
	H.M.I. Lights (A.C. Power)									
	H.M.I. Bulb Time									
	Box Rental									
	Additional Equipment									
40	Equipment Purchases									
	Globes and Carbons									
	Fuses, Plugs, Tapes, Other Expendables									
	Generator Gas & Oil									
85	Additional Expense									
95	Miscellaneous									
99	Loss, Damage, Repair									
						SUBTOTALS				
						TOTAL ACCT 3300				

A - Fringeable/Taxable
B - Non-Fringeable/Taxable
C - Non-Taxable

PROD. NO. _____   PROD. TITLE _____   DATE:_____

3400 WARDROBE DEPARTMENT

ACCT. NO.	DESCRIPTION	LOCAL/ ON LOC.	DAYS/WEEKS				RATE	SUBTOTALS		
			PREP	SHOOT	WRAP	TOTAL		A	B	C
01	Costume Designer	Local								
		On Loc.								
02	Asst. To Costume Designer	Local								
		On Loc.								
		Local								
		On Loc.								
05	Women's Costumer	Local								
		On Loc.								
06	Women's Costumer—Set	Local								
		On Loc.								
		Local								
		On Loc.								
		Local								
		On Loc.								
07	Men's Costumer	Local								
		On Loc.								
08	Men's Costumer—Set	Local								
		On Loc.								
09	Tailor	Local								
		On Loc.								
10	Seamstress	Local								
		On Loc.								
		Local								
		On Loc.								
	Additional Hire	Local								
		On Loc.								
30	Rentals (See Wardrobe Detail Page 23A)									
	Box Rental									
40	Purchases (See Wardrobe Detail Page 23A)									
	Manufacturing									
	Equipment									
	Alteration Material									
45	Dry Cleaning and Laundry									
85	Additional Expense									
95	Miscellaneous									
99	Loss, Damage, Repair									
						SUBTOTALS				
						TOTAL ACCT 3400				

A - Fringeable/Taxable
B - Non-Fringeable/Taxable
C - Non-Taxable

PROD. NO. _____ PROD. TITLE _____ DATE:_____

ACCTS 3430 & 3440   WARDROBE—DETAIL

CAST NO.	SCENE NAME/NO. CHARACTER	QTY	ITEM DESCRIPTION	RENTALS TIME	RATE	AMOUNT	PURCHASES AMOUNT	✔
				SUBTOTALS				
			TOTAL DETAIL ACCTS 3430 & 3440				

A - Fringeable/Taxable   C - Non-Taxable
B - Non-Fringeable/Taxable   ✔ - Recoupable

PROD. NO. _____   PROD. TITLE _____   DATE:_____

3500   MAKEUP and HAIRDRESSING DEPARTMENT

ACCT. NO.	DESCRIPTION	LOCAL/ ON LOC.	DAYS/WEEKS				RATE	SUBTOTALS		
			PREP	SHOOT	WRAP	TOTAL		A	B	C
01	1st Makeup Artist	Local								
		On Loc.								
02	2nd Makeup Artist	Local								
		On Loc.								
03	Makeup Assistant	Local								
		On Loc.								
		Local								
		On Loc.								
05	Body Makeup	Local								
		On Loc.								
		Local								
		On Loc.								
	Additional Hire	Local								
		On Loc.								
		Local								
		On Loc.								
10	1st Hairstylist	Local								
		On Loc.								
11	2nd Hairstylist	Local								
		On Loc.								
12	Hairstylist Asst.	Local								
		On Loc.								
	Additional Hire	Local								
		On Loc.								
		Local								
		On Loc.								
30	Rentals									
	Equipment, Tables, Chairs, Mirrors									
	Box Rentals									
40	Purchases									
	Lights, Bulbs									
	Makeup Supplies									
	Hairdressing Supplies									
	Wigs and Hairpieces									
85	Additional Expense									
95	Miscellaneous									
99	Loss, Damage, Repair									
						SUBTOTALS				
						TOTAL ACCT 3500				

A - Fringeable/Taxable
B - Non-Fringeable/Taxable
C - Non-Taxable

©1984 Lone Eagle Productions, Inc.

PROD. NO. _____ PROD. TITLE _____ DATE:_____

ACCTS 3530 & 3540 MAKEUP AND HAIRDRESSING—DETAIL

CAST NO.	SCENE NAME/NO. CHARACTER	ITEM		RENTALS			PURCHASES	✔
		QTY	DESCRIPTION	TIME	RATE	AMOUNT	AMOUNT	
				SUBTOTALS				
			TOTAL DETAIL ACCTS 3530 & 3540				

A - Fringeable/Taxable   C - Non-Taxable
B - Non-Fringeable/Taxable   ✔ - Recoupable

©1984 Lone Eagle Productions, Inc.

PROD. NO. _____   PROD. TITLE _____   DATE:_____

3600 SET OPERATIONS

ACCT. NO.	DESCRIPTION	LOCAL/ ON LOC.	DAYS/WEEKS				RATE	SUBTOTALS		
			PREP	SHOOT	WRAP	TOTAL		A	B	C
01	Caterer/Driver	Local								
		On Loc.								
02	Caterer/Asst.	Local								
		On Loc.								
04	Craft Service	Local								
		On Loc.								
05	First Aid/ Nurse	Local								
		On Loc.								
06	Doctor	Local								
		On Loc.								
07	Police	Local								
		On Loc.								
08	Firemen	Local								
		On Loc.								
09	Guards/ Watchmen	Local								
		On Loc.								
	Additional Hire	Local								
		On Loc.								
10	Police Vehicle Expense									
11	Ambulance									
15	Fire Equipment									
20	Catering Costs (No. People x No. Days x Rate)									
	Coffee, Rolls, etc.									
	Breakfast									
	Lunch									
	Dinner									
	Soft Drinks, etc.									
	Tables, Chairs									
	Taxes									
	Caterer-Mileage (Travel & Living See Location Acct 4000)									
	Hotel & Restaurant Gratuities									
						SUBTOTALS THIS PAGE				
						CONTINUED ON NEXT PAGE				

A - Fringeable/Taxable
B - Non-Fringeable/Taxable
C - Non-Taxable

PROD. NO. _____ PROD. TITLE _____ DATE:_____

3600	SET OPERATIONS — (CONT'D)	SUBTOTALS		
ACCT. NO.	DESCRIPTION	A	B	C
25	Courtesy Payments			
26	Weather Service			
27	Portable Toilets (Weeks x Rate)			
29	Transportation Fee			
30	Rentals (Weeks x Rate)			
	Craftservice Box			
	Dolly, Dolly Track, Crane (See Grip Dept. Acct 3200)			
	Grip Package & Grip Box (See Grip Dept. Acct 3200)			
	Camera Platform, Planes, Helicopters, Trains, Boats, etc.			
	(See Special Equipment Acct 3000)			
	Paint Box (See Set Dressing Dept. Acct 2400)			
	Greens (See Set Dressing Dept. Acct 2400)			
40	Purchases (Weeks x Rate)			
	Craftservice			
	Greens (See Set Dressing Acct 2400)			
	Paint (See Set Dressing Acct 2400)			
85	Additional Expenses			
95	Miscellaneous			
99	Loss, Damage, Repair			
	SUBTOTALS FROM PREVIOUS PAGE			
	SUBTOTALS THIS PAGE			
	TOTAL ACCT 3600			

A - Fringeable/Taxable
B - Non-Fringeable/Taxable
C - Non-Taxable

PROD. NO. _____ PROD. TITLE _____ DATE:_____

3700	LOCAL SITE RENTAL EXPENSE	SUBTOTALS		
ACCT. NO.	DESCRIPTION	A	B	C
01	Site Contact/Broker			
	Location Manager (See Acct 2000)			
03	Site Rental (See Detail Page 27A)			
04	Survey Costs — Scouting			
	Mileage			
	Gas/Oil			
08	Gratuities			
09	Meals			
17	Courtesy Payments (See Also Accts 6204 and 3625)			
25	Permits, Fees, etc. (See Detail Page 27A)			
27	Parking (Crew and Equipment)			
	Medical, Police, Fireman, etc. (See Set Operations Acct 3600)			
32	Messenger Service			
35	Janitorial			
	Additional Hire			
85	Additional Expenses			
95	Miscellaneous			
99	Loss, Damage, Repair			
	SUBTOTALS			
	TOTAL ACCT 3700			

A - Fringeable/Taxable   C - Non-Taxable
B - Non-Fringeable/Taxable

PROD. NO. _____ PROD. TITLE _____ DATE:_____

3703 LOCAL SITE RENTAL—DETAIL

SET NO.	SCENE NAME/NO.	PREP			SHOOT			STRIKE			PERMITS, FEES	TOTALS
		TIME	RATE	AMT.	TIME	RATE	AMT.	TIME	RATE	AMT.		
	SUBTOTALS											

TOTAL DETAIL ACCT 3703

A - Fringeable/Taxable   C - Non-Taxable
B - Non-Fringeable/Taxable

©1984 Lone Eagle Productions, Inc.

PROD. NO. _____ PROD. TITLE _____ DATE: _____

3800	STAGE RENTAL AND EXPENSE				SUBTOTALS		
ACCT. NO.	DESCRIPTION	TIME	RATE	AMT.	A	B	C
01	Guards						
02	Lot Man (Local 40)						
03	Utility Person						
	Additional Hire						
05	Power						
06	Equipment Package						
	Grip						
	Electrical						
	Cherry Picker						
	Forklift, etc.						
30	Rental						
	(See Detail Page 28A)						
65	Office Rental						
70	Telephone						
85	Additional Expenses						
95	Miscellaneous						
99	Loss, Damage, Repair						
			SUBTOTALS				
			TOTAL ACCT 3800				

A - Fringeable/Taxable   C - Non-Taxable
B - Non-Fringeable/Taxable

©1984 Lone Eagle Productions, Inc.

PROD. NO. _____

PROD. TITLE _____

DATE: _____

3830 STAGE RENTAL—DETAIL

SET NO.	SCENE NAME/NUMBER	CONSTRUCTION		REHEARSAL		HOLD		TEST		SHOOT		STRIKE		TOTAL	
		TIME	RATE	TIME	RATE	TIME	RATE	TIME	RATE	TIME	RATE	TIME	RATE	TIME	AMOUNT
SUBTOTALS															

TOTAL DETAIL ACCT 3830

A - Fringeable/Taxable
B - Non-Fringeable/Taxable
C - Non-Taxable

PROD. NO. _____ PROD. TITLE _____ DATE:_____

4000 LOCATION EXPENSE

ACCT. NO.	DESCRIPTION	TIME	RATE	AMT.	A	B	C
					SUBTOTALS		
01	Location Contact/Broker						
	Location Mgr. (See Acct 2000)						
	Interpreters (See Acct 2000)						
02	Location Site Rental (See Detail 30A)						
03	Permits						
04	Scouting Costs (See Detail 30B)						
	Travel and Living (See Detail Page 30B)						
	Local Contact						
	Vehicle Rentals						
	Additional Expenses						
05	Transportation to Location						
	(See Detail 30C)						
06	Flight Insurance						
07	Passports, Visas and Work Permits						
08	Travel Gratuities & Excess Baggage						
09	Travel and Living (See Detail Page 30C)						
	Travel						
	Lodging						
	Meals						
	Catering Costs						
	(See Set Operations Acct 3600)						
10	Shipping Costs (Also See Acct 6203)						
	Custom and Brokerage Fees						
	Export Taxes						
	Equipment Shipment						
	Loading and Unloading Crates						
	Packing/Crating, Labor & Materials						
	Film Shipments						
	Air Freight						
	Airport Pickups & Deliveries						
	SUBTOTALS						

CONTINUED ON NEXT PAGE

A - Fringeable/Taxable C - Non-Taxable
B - Non-Fringeable/Taxable

© 1984 Lone Eagle Productions, Inc.

PROD. NO. _____ PROD. TITLE _____ DATE:_____

4000	LOCATION EXPENSE—(Cont'd)	SUBTOTALS		
ACCT. NO.	DESCRIPTION	A	B	C
11	Postage (Also See Acct 6240)			
12	Office Supplies (Also See Acct 6240)			
13	Office Rental (Also See Acct 6230)			
14	Office Equipment and Furniture Rental (Also See Acct 6230)			
15	Special Equipment			
16	Telephone and Telegraph (Also See Acct 6230)			
	Installation Charges			
17	Courtesy Payments (Also See Acct 6204 & 3625)			
18	Government Censors			
19	Location Weather Service			
22	Local Projection Service			
25	Permits (Props and Special Effects)			
26	Storage/Working Space Rental			
	Wardrobe			
	Makeup/Hair			
	Carpentry			
	Prop			
	Set Dressing			
	Special Effects			
	General Storage			
	Vehicles (See Transportation Acct 4600)			
27	Parking			
	Location Medical, Police, Firemen			
	Watchmen (See Set Operations Acct 3600)			
28	Messenger Service			
29	Janitorial/Cleaning			
35	Hotel and Restaurant Gratuities			
85	Additional Expenses			
95	Miscellaneous			
99	Loss, Damage, Repair			
	SUBTOTALS FROM PREVIOUS PAGE			
	SUBTOTALS THIS PAGE			
	TOTAL ACCT 4000			

A - Fringeable/Taxable   C - Non-Taxable
B - Non-Fringeable/Taxable

©1984 Lone Eagle Productions, Inc.

PROD. NO. _____   PROD. TITLE _____   DATE:_____

4002   LOCATION SITE RENTAL—DETAIL

SET NO.	SCENE NAME/NO.	PREP			SHOOT			STRIKE			PERMITS, FEES	TOTALS
		TIME	RATE	AMT.	TIME	RATE	AMT.	TIME	RATE	AMT.		
	SUBTOTALS											
							TOTAL DETAIL ACCT 4002					

A - Fringeable/Taxable
B - Non-Fringeable/Taxable
C - Non-Taxable

4004 SCOUTING COSTS — TRAVEL AND LIVING

POSITION/NAME	DESTINATION (RT)	AIRFARES			LODGING (PER DIEM)			MEALS (PER DIEM)				TOTALS
		NO. FLIGHTS	RATE	SUBTOTAL	NO. DAYS	RATE	SUBTOTAL	NO. DAYS		RATE	SUBTOTAL	
									B			
									L			
									D			
									B			
									L			
									D			
									B			
									L			
									D			
									B			
									L			
									D			
									B			
									L			
									D			
									B			
									L			
									D			
									B			
									L			
									D			
									B			
									L			
									D			
SUBTOTALS												TOTAL DETAIL ACCT 4004

A - Fringeable/Taxable
B - Non-Fringeable/Taxable
C - Non-Taxable

©1984 Lone Eagle Productions, Inc.

PROD. NO. _____ PROD. TITLE _____ DATE: _____

4005 ON LOCATION—TRAVEL AND LIVING

POSITION/NAME	DESTINATION (RT)	AIRFARES			LODGING (PER DIEM)			MEALS (PER DIEM)			TOTALS
		NO. FLIGHTS	RATE	SUBTOTAL	NO. DAYS	RATE	SUBTOTAL	NO. DAYS	RATE	SUBTOTAL	
								B L D			
								B L D			
								B L D			
								B L D			
								B L D			
								B L D			
								B L D			
								B L D			
SUBTOTALS											
										TOTAL DETAIL ACCT 4005	

A - Fringeable/Taxable
B - Non-Fringeable/Taxable
C - Non-Taxable

PROD. NO. _____ PROD. TITLE _____ DATE: _____

4100 SECOND UNIT—SUMMARY

ACCT NO.	DESCRIPTION	PAGE NO.	BUDGET	TOTALS
01	Director (See Acct 1202)	32A		
02	Choreographer	32A		
03	Dialogue Director	32A		
04	Cast	32A		
19	Fringe Benefits & Payroll Taxes	32A		
	TOTAL SECOND UNIT ABOVE THE LINE			
20	Production Department	32A		
21	Extra Talent	32B		
22	Art Department	32B		
23	Set Construction	32B		
24	Set Dressing	32B		
25	Prop Department	32B		
26	Picture Vehicles	32B		
27	Special Effects	32B		
28	Camera Department	32B		
31	Sound Department	32C		
32	Grip Department	32C		
33	Lighting Department	32C		
34	Wardrobe	32C		
35	Makeup & Hair Dressing	32C		
36	Set Operations	32C		
40	Location Expenses	32D		
	SUBTOTAL THIS PAGE			

(CONTINUED ON NEXT PAGE)

PROD. NO. _____ PROD. TITLE _____ DATE:_____

| 4100 | SECOND UNIT—SUMMARY (Cont'd) | | | |

ACCT NO.	DESCRIPTION	PAGE NO.	BUDGET	TOTALS
45	Animals	32D		
46	Transportation	32E		
47	Film/Sound & Lab	32E		
48	Expenses (Rentals & Purchases)	32F		
49	Fringe Benefits & Payroll Taxes	32G		
85	Additional Expenses	32G		
95	Miscellaneous	32G		
99	Loss, Damage & Repair	32G		

SUBTOTALS THIS PAGE	
SUBTOTALS FROM PREVIOUS PAGE	
TOTAL SECOND UNIT BELOW THE LINE	
TOTAL SECOND UNIT ABOVE THE LINE	

TOTAL ACCOUNT 4100 [ ]

PROD. NO. _____ PROD. TITLE _____ DATE:_____

4100	SECOND UNIT

NO.	TITLE	DAYS					SUBTOTALS		
		PREP	SHOOT	WRAP	TOTAL	RATE	A	B	C
01	Director								
02	Choreographer								
03	Dialogue Director								
							TOTAL		

04	CAST NAME & STUNTS	DAYS					SUBTOTALS		
		PREP	SHOOT	WRAP	TOTAL	RATE	A	B	C
	Welfare Worker/Teacher								
							TOTAL		

19	FRINGE BENEFITS & PAYROLL TAXES/ABOVE-THE-LINE SECOND UNIT	AMOUNT	TOTALS
	Payroll Taxes & Comp. Ins.		
	Pension		
	Health & Welfare		

TOTAL SECOND UNIT ABOVE THE LINE	

20	PRODUCTION DEPARTMENT	DAYS					SUBTOTALS		
		PREP	SHOOT	WRAP	TOTAL	RATE	A	B	C
	Production Mgr.								
	1st Asst. Director								
	2nd Asst. Director								
	Location Mgr.								
	Production Acct.								
	D.G.A. Trainee								
	P.A.'s								
	Script Supervisor								
	Prod. Office Coord.								
	Additional Clerical								
	Technical Advisor								
							TOTAL		

TOTAL	

©1984 Lone Eagle Productions, Inc.

PROD. NO. _____   PROD. TITLE _____   DATE:_____

4100	SECOND UNIT—(Cont'd)											

21 EXTRA TALENT

DAY NO.	NO.	RATE	DAY NO.	NO.	RATE	DAY NO.	NO.	RATE		A	B	C
										\multicolumn{3}{c}{SUBTOTALS}	
1			4			7						
2			5			8						
3			6			9						
									TOTAL			

22 ART DEPARTMENT

	PREP	SHOOT	WRAP	TOTAL	RATE	A	B	C
Prod. Designer								
Art Director								
					TOTAL			

23 SET CONSTRUCTION

	PREP	SHOOT	WRAP	TOTAL	RATE	A	B	C
Const. Coordinator								
Const. Labor								
					TOTAL			

24 SET DRESSING

	PREP	SHOOT	WRAP	TOTAL	RATE	A	B	C
Set Decorator								
Swing Gang-Leadman								
					TOTAL			

25 PROP DEPARTMENT

	PREP	SHOOT	WRAP	TOTAL	RATE	A	B	C
Prop Master								
Asst. Propmaster								
					TOTAL			

26 PICTURE VEHICLES

	PREP	SHOOT	WRAP	TOTAL	RATE	A	B	C
Vehicle #1 Driver/Owner								
Vehicle #2 Driver/Owner								
Vehicle #3 Driver/Owner								
					TOTAL			

27 SPECIAL EFFECTS DEPT.

	PREP	SHOOT	WRAP	TOTAL	RATE	A	B	C
Special Effects Man								
					TOTAL			

28 CAMERA DEPARTMENT

	PREP	SHOOT	WRAP	TOTAL	RATE	A	B	C
Director of Photography								
Camera Operator								
1st A. C.								
2nd A. C.								
					TOTAL			

PROD. NO. _____   PROD. TITLE _____   DATE:_____

4100 SECOND UNIT—(Cont'd)

31 SOUND DEPARTMENT

	DAYS					SUBTOTALS		
	PREP	SHOOT	WRAP	TOTAL	RATE	A	B	C
Mixer								
Boom Operator								
						TOTAL		

32 GRIP DEPARTMENT

	DAYS					SUBTOTALS		
	PREP	SHOOT	WRAP	TOTAL	RATE	A	B	C
Key Grip								
2nd Company Grip								
Company Grip								
						TOTAL		

33 LIGHTING DEPARTMENT

	DAYS					SUBTOTALS		
	PREP	SHOOT	WRAP	TOTAL	RATE	A	B	C
Gaffer								
Best Boy								
Electrician								
						TOTAL		

34 WARDROBE DEPARTMENT

	DAYS					SUBTOTALS		
	PREP	SHOOT	WRAP	TOTAL	RATE	A	B	C
Designer								
Wardrobe Woman								
Wardrobe Man								
						TOTAL		

35 MAKE-UP AND HAIRDRESSING

	DAYS					SUBTOTALS		
	PREP	SHOOT	WRAP	TOTAL	RATE	A	B	C
Make-up Artist								
Hair Stylist								
						TOTAL		

36 SET OPERATIONS

	DAYS					SUBTOTALS		
	PREP	SHOOT	WRAP	TOTAL	RATE	A	B	C
Craft Serviceman								
Policeman								
Fireman								
Watchman								
First Aid/Nurse								
Doctor								
						TOTAL		

PROD. NO. _____ PROD. TITLE _____ DATE:_____

4100	SECOND UNIT — (Cont'd)								

40	LOCATION EXPENSE	DAYS					SUBTOTALS		
		PREP	SHOOT	WRAP	TOTAL	RATE	A	B	C
	Location Contact								
	Interpreters								
	Location Site Rental								
							TOTAL		

45	ANIMALS	DAYS					SUBTOTALS		
		PREP	SHOOT	WRAP	TOTAL	RATE	A	B	C
	Animals								
	Wrangler/Trainer								
							TOTAL		

46A	TRANSPORTATION (LABOR)	DAYS					SUBTOTALS		
		PREP	SHOOT	WRAP	TOTAL	RATE	A	B	C
	Driver 1								
	Driver 2								
	Driver 3								
	Driver 4								
	Driver 5								
	Driver 6								
	Driver 7								
	Driver 8								
							TOTAL		

46 TRANSPORTATION, LODGING, MEALS—SECOND UNIT

POSITION/NAME	DESTINATION (RT)	AIRFARES			LODGING (PER DIEM)			MEALS (PER DIEM)				TOTALS
		NO. FLIGHTS	RATE	SUBTOTAL	NO. DAYS	RATE	SUBTOTAL	NO. DAYS		RATE	SUBTOTAL	
									B			
									L			
									D			
									B			
									L			
									D			
									B			
									L			
									D			
									B			
									L			
									D			
									B			
									L			
									D			
									B			
									L			
									D			
									B			
									L			
									D			
									B			
									L			
									D			
SUBTOTALS												TOTAL DETAIL ACCT 46

A - Fringeable/Taxable
B - Non-Fringeable/Taxable
C - Non-Taxable

© 1984 Lone Eagle Productions, Inc.

PROD. NO. _____ PROD. TITLE _____ DATE:_____

4100	SECOND UNIT—(Cont'd)	

48A EQUIPMENT AND MATERIALS/RENTALS

DEPARTMENT	DESCRIPTION	SUBTOTAL
		TOTAL

48B EQUIPMENT AND MATERIALS/PURCHASES

DEPARTMENT	DESCRIPTION	SUBTOTAL
		TOTAL

© 1984 Lone Eagle Productions, Inc.

PROD. NO. _____   PROD. TITLE _____   DATE:_____

4100	SECOND UNIT—(Cont'd)

49	FRINGE BENEFITS AND PAYROLL TAXES (2ND UNIT)

DESCRIPTION	PAYROLL	PENSION	HEALTH & WELFARE	TOTALS
DGA $ _____	% ____	% ____	% ____	
PGA $ _____	% ____	% ____	% ____	
WGA $ _____	% ____	% ____	% ____	
SAG $ _____	% ____	% ____	% ____	
IATSE $ _____	% ____	% ____	% ____	
NABET $ _____	% ____	% ____	% ____	
OTHER OR ALLOW $ _____	% ____	% ____	% ____	
SUBTOTALS				

85	ADDITIONAL EXPENSES	
		TOTAL

95	MISCELLANEOUS	
		TOTAL

99	LOSS, DAMAGE, REPAIR	
		TOTAL

TOTAL SECOND UNIT BELOW-THE-LINE	
TOTAL SECOND UNIT ABOVE-THE-LINE	

TOTAL ACCT 4100	

| PROD. NO. _____ | PROD. TITLE _____ | DATE:_____ |

4200	**TESTS** (USE SECOND UNIT FOR DETAILED TEST BUDGET — ACCT 4100)		**SUBTOTALS**		
ACCT. NO.	**DESCRIPTION**		**A**	**B**	**C**
47	Film/Sound Lab				
	Negative Film				
	Sound Negative				
	Film Negative Develop				
	Film One Light Print				
	Color Corrected Dailies				
	Sound Transfers—Stock				
	Sound Transfers—Labor				
85	Additional Expenses				
95	Miscellaneous				
99	Loss, Damage, Repair				
	SUBTOTALS				
	TOTAL ACCT 4200				

A - Fringeable/Taxable C - Non-Taxable
B - Non-Fringeable/Taxable

©1984 Lone Eagle Productions, Inc.

PROD. NO. _____ PROD. TITLE _____ DATE:_____

4300 MINIATURE DEPARTMENT

ACCT. NO.	DESCRIPTION		NO.	LOCAL/ ON LOC.	DAYS/WEEKS				RATE	SUBTOTALS		
					PREP	SHOOT	WRAP	TOTAL		A	B	C
01	Supervisor			Local								
				On Loc.								
	Labor		No.	Local								
				On Loc.								
05	Painters			Local								
				On Loc.								
				Local								
				On Loc.								
06	Scenic Artists			Local								
				On Loc.								
				Local								
				On Loc.								
07	Carpenters			Local								
				On Loc.								
				Local								
				On Loc.								
08	Propmakers			Local								
				On Loc.								
				Local								
				On Loc.								
				Local								
				On Loc.								
				Local								
				On Loc.								
	Additional Hire			Local								
				On Loc.								
15	Labor (See Detail Page 34A)											
20	Materials (See Detail Page 34A)											
22	Rigging (See Detail Page 34A)											
24	Striking (See Detail Page 34A)											
30	Rentals (See Detail Page 34B)											
40	Purchases (See Detail Page 34B)											
85	Additional Expense											
95	Miscellaneous											
99	Loss, Damage, Repair											
								SUBTOTALS				
								TOTAL ACCT 4300				

A - Fringeable/Taxable
B - Non-Fringeable/Taxable
C - Non-Taxable

©1984 Lone Eagle Productions, Inc.

PROD. NO. _____   PROD. TITLE _____   DATE:_____

SET NO.	SCENE NAME/NO. DESCRIPTION	(4315) LABOR	(4320) MATERIALS	(4322) RIGGING	(4324) STRIKING	A	B	C
	SUBTOTALS							
	TOTAL DETAIL ACCT 4315, 4320, 4322, 4324							

4315, 4320, 4322, 4324   MINIATURES—DETAIL   SUBTOTALS

A - Fringeable/Taxable
B - Non-Fringeable/Taxable
C - Non-Taxable

PROD. NO. _____ PROD. TITLE _____ DATE:_____

ACCTS 4330 & 4340 MINIATURES—DETAIL

SET NO.	SCENE NAME/NO. DESCRIPTION	QTY	ITEM DESCRIPTION	RENTALS			PURCHASES	✔
				TIME	RATE	AMOUNT	AMOUNT	
				SUBTOTALS				
			TOTAL DETAIL ACCTS 4330 & 4340				

A - Fringeable/Taxable   C - Non-Taxable
B - Non-Fringeable/Taxable   ✔ - Recoupable

PROD. NO. _____ PROD. TITLE _____ DATE:_____

4400 PROCESS DEPARTMENT

ACCT. NO.	DESCRIPTION	LOCAL/ ON LOC.	DAYS/WEEKS				RATE	SUBTOTALS		
			PREP	SHOOT	WRAP	TOTAL		A	B	C
01	Projectionist	Local								
		On Loc.								
		Local								
		On Loc.								
02	Camera Man	Local								
		On Loc.								
		Local								
		On Loc.								
03	Camera Operator	Local								
		On Loc.								
		Local								
		On Loc.								
04	Asst. Camera Man	Local								
		On Loc.								
		Local								
		On Loc.								
05	Electrical	Local								
		On Loc.								
06	Grip	Local								
		On Loc.								
07	Matte Artist	Local								
		On Loc.								
08	Matte Crew	Local								
		On Loc.								
		Local								
		On Loc.								
09	Rear Screen									
10	Front Screen									
12	Mock Up									
30	Rentals									
40	Purchases									
85	Additional Expense									
95	Miscellaneous									
99	Loss, Damage, Repair									
						SUBTOTALS				
						TOTAL ACCT 4400				

A - Fringeable/Taxable
B - Non-Fringeable/Taxable
C - Non-Taxable

PROD. NO. _____ PROD. TITLE _____ DATE:_____

4500 ANIMALS

ACCT. NO.	DESCRIPTION	LOCAL/ ON LOC.	DAYS/WEEKS				RATE	SUBTOTALS		
			PREP	SHOOT	WRAP	TOTAL		A	B	C
01	Head Wrangler	Local								
		On Loc.								
02	Additional Wrangler	Local								
		On Loc.								
03	Trainers	Local								
		On Loc.								
		Local								
		On Loc.								
04	Handlers	Local								
		On Loc.								
		Local								
		On Loc.								
		Local								
		On Loc.								
		Local								
		On Loc.								
		Local								
		On Loc.								
		Local								
		On Loc.								
		Local								
		On Loc.								
	Additional Hire	Local								
		On Loc.								
30	Rentals (See Detail Page 36A)									
40	Purchases (See Detail Page 36A)									
50	Animal Maintenance									
60	Special Transportation									
75	Travel and Living (List on Acct 4005)									
85	Additional Expense									
95	Miscellaneous									
99	Loss, Damage, Repair									
						SUBTOTALS				
						TOTAL ACCT 4500				

A - Fringeable/Taxable
B - Non-Fringeable/Taxable
C - Non-Taxable

PROD. NO. _____ PROD. TITLE _____ DATE:_____

ACCTS 4530 & 4540 ANIMALS—DETAIL

SET NO.	SCENE NAME/NO. DESCRIPTION	QTY	ANIMALS DESCRIPTION	W/H/T	RENTALS RATE	AMOUNT	PURCHASES AMOUNT	✔
			SUBTOTALS					
		TOTAL DETAIL ACCTS NO. 4530 & 4540					

A - Fringeable/Taxable   ✔ = Recoupable
B - Non-Fringeable/Taxable   W/H/T = Wrangler, Handler or Trainer
C - Non-Taxable

PROD. NO. _____ PROD. TITLE _____ DATE:_____

4600	TRANSPORTATION DEPARTMENT	SUBTOTALS		
ACCT. NO.	DESCRIPTION	A	B	C
01	Coordinator			
02	Drivers—Captain and Co-Captain (See Detail Pages 37 A & B)			
03	Drivers (See Detail Pages 37 A & B)			
30	Vehicles—Rentals/Local (See Detail Pages 37 A & B)			
35	Vehicles—Rentals/Location (See Detail Pages 37 A & B)			
50	Gas and Oil			
55	Gas and Oil — Generator			
57	Messenger Service			
59	Deliveries and Pick-Ups			
60	Pick-Up — Dailies (Also See Location Acct 4000)			
61	Taxis and Limos			
63	Car Allowances (See Detail Page 37D)			
65	Vehicle Mileage (See Detail Page 37B)			
67	Mileage Allowances — Crew and Cast (See Detail Page 37E)			
69	Permits, Tolls, Parking and Fees (See Detail Page 37B)			
70	Maintenance (See Detail Page 37B)			
71	Storage			
73	Trucks to Distant Location—Expenses			
75	Truck Rigging/Shelving			
85	Additional Expenses			
95	Miscellaneous			
99	Loss, Damage, Repair			
	SUBTOTALS			
	TOTAL ACCT 4600			

A - Fringeable/Taxable   C - Non-Taxable
B - Non-Fringeable/Taxable

©1984 Lone Eagle Productions, Inc.

NOTE: For varying times and rates indicate PREP/SHOOT/WRAP

DESCRIPTION	DRIVERS LOCAL WEEKS	RATE	LOCATION WEEKS	RATE	TOTAL	EQUIPMENT LOCAL WEEKS	RATE	LOCATION WEEKS	RATE	TOTAL
Coordinator										
Captain										
Co-Captain										
Dispatcher				4601 Total						
Mechanic										
Production Van (Grip/Electric)										
Camera/Sound Truck										
Prop Truck										
Special Effects Truck										
Wardrobe Truck										
Wardrobe Trailer										
Makeup/Hair Truck										
Makeup/Hair Trailer				4602 Total						
Construction Crew Cab										
Construction Truck										
Set Dressing Wagon										
Set Dressing Truck										
Honeywagons										
Motor Homes										
Station Wagons										
Crew Bus										
Extra Bus										
Mini Vans/Crew Cab										
People Mover										
Catering Truck (Fee)				4603 Total			4630 Sub.			4635 Sub.
				CONTINUED ON NEXT PAGE			CONTINUED ON NEXT PAGE			

NOTE: For varying times and rates indicate PREP/SHOOT/WRAP

| | DRIVERS | | | | | EQUIPMENT | | | | |
| | LOCAL | | LOCATION | | | LOCAL | | LOCATION | | |
DESCRIPTION	WEEKS	RATE	WEEKS	RATE	TOTAL	WEEKS	RATE	WEEKS	RATE	TOTAL
Limo										
Camera Car/Insert Car										
Car Carrier										
Water Wagon										
Pick-up Trucks										
Crane Driver										
Fuel Truck										
Ambulance (See Location Acct 4000)										
Fork Lift										
Tow Trucks										
Generator										
Other Production Cars										
Additional Hire										
Subtotal From Previous Page										
TOTAL DETAIL 4603										
					Total Det. 4630			Total Det. 4635		
65 Vehicle Mileage										
69 Permits, Tolls, Parking and Fees										
70 Maintenance										
71 Storage										

© 1984 Lone Eagle Productions, Inc.

TRANSPORTATION—DETAIL

NOTE: For varying times and rates indicate PREP/SHOOT/WRAP

| DESCRIPTION | DRIVERS | | | | | EQUIPMENT | | | |
| | LOCAL | | LOCATION | | | LOCAL | | LOCATION | |
	WEEKS	RATE	WEEKS	RATE	TOTAL	WEEKS	RATE	WEEKS	RATE	TOTAL

© 1984 Lone Eagle Productions, Inc.

PROD. NO. _____ PROD. TITLE _____ DATE:_____

4663 CAR ALLOWANCES—DETAIL

DEPARTMENT	POSTION/NAME	WEEKS/DAYS	RATE	TOTAL
	TOTAL DETAIL ACCT 3400			

A - Fringeable/Taxable
B - Non-Fringeable/Taxable
C - Non-Taxable

PROD. NO. _____ PROD. TITLE _____ DATE: _____

4667 MILEAGE—DETAIL

DAY NO.	NO. PEOPLE	SET NO./LOCATION	MILES	RATE	TOTAL
		TOTAL DETAIL ACCT 4667			

A - Fringeable/Taxable
B - Non-Fringeable/Taxable
C - Non-Taxable

PROD. NO. _____ PROD. TITLE _____ DATE:_____

4700 PRODUCTION RAWSTOCK AND LABORATORY					SUBTOTALS		
ACCT. NO.	DESCRIPTION	FOOTAGE	RATE	AMOUNT	A	B	C
01	Picture Negative Rawstock						
	1/4" Audio Tape Rawstock						
10	Picture Negative Developing						
	Forced Developing						
20	Picture Negative Print						
	One Lite Print						
	Color Corrected Dailies						
35	Sound Transfer						
	Stock						
	Labor						
45	Video						
	Video Tape Rawstock						
	Film to Tape Transfer						
	3/4" Tape Time Code Copies						
50	Special Lab Work						
85	Additional Expenses						
90	Sales Tax on Acct 4700						
95	Miscellaneous						
	Reels, Cases, Boxes, Etc.						
	Picture Leader						
99	Loss, Damage, Repair						
				SUBTOTALS			
			TOTAL ACCT 4700				

A - Fringeable/Taxable   C - Non-Taxable
B - Non-Fringeable/Taxable

©1984 Lone Eagle Productions, Inc.

PROD. NO. _____   PROD. TITLE _____   DATE:_____

4900   FRINGE BENEFITS AND PAYROLL TAXES—BELOW-THE-LINE

ACCT NO.	DESCRIPTION	PAYROLL	PENSION	HEALTH & WELFARE	TOTALS
01	DGA $ _____	% _____	% _____	% _____	
02	PGA $ _____	% _____	% _____	% _____	
03	WGA $ _____	% _____	% _____	% _____	
04	SAG $ _____	% _____	% _____	% _____	
05	IATSE $ _____	% _____	% _____	% _____	
06	NABET $ _____	% _____	% _____	% _____	
07	OTHER $ _____	% _____	% _____	% _____	
10	or Allow				

SUBTOTALS [   ] [   ] [   ] [   ]

TOTAL ACCT 4900 [   ]

TOTAL COST BELOW-THE-LINE [   ]

A - Fringeable/Taxable
B - Non-Fringeable/Taxable
C - Non-Taxable

PROD. NO. _____   PROD. TITLE _____   DATE:_____

5000   FILM EDITING DEPARTMENT

ACCT. NO.	DESCRIPTION	LOCAL/ ON LOC.	DAYS/WEEKS				RATE	SUBTOTALS		
			PREP	SHOOT	WRAP	TOTAL		A	B	C
01	Post Production Supervisor	Local								
		On Loc.								
		Local								
		On Loc.								
02	Editor	Local								
		On Loc.								
		Local								
		On Loc.								
03	Asst. Editors	Local								
		On Loc.								
		Local								
		On Loc.								
04	Apprentice Editor	Local								
		On Loc.								
		Local								
		On Loc.								
05	Looping Editors	Local								
		On Loc.								
06	Asst. Looping Editor	Local								
		On Loc.								
		Local								
		On Loc.								
08	Music Editor	Local								
		On Loc.								
09	Asst. Music Editor	Local								
		On Loc.								
		SUBTOTALS THIS PAGE								
		CONTINUED ON NEXT PAGE								

A - Fringeable/Taxable
B - Non-Fringeable/Taxable
C - Non-Taxable

PROD. NO. _____   PROD. TITLE _____   DATE:_____

5000 FILM EDITING DEPARTMENT—(Cont'd)

ACCT. NO.	DESCRIPTION	LOCAL/ ON LOC.	DAYS/WEEKS				RATE	SUBTOTALS		
			PREP	SHOOT	WRAP	TOTAL		A	B	C
07	Sound Effects Editor & Asst.	Local								
		On Loc.								
		Local								
		On Loc.								
08	Projection Labor	Local								
		On Loc.								
		Local								
		On Loc.								
09	Dialogue Transcription	Local								
		On Loc.								
11	Off Line Editing-Labor	Local								
		On Loc.								
12	Cutting Continuity	Local								
		On Loc.								
13	Secretary	Local								
		On Loc.								
14	Librarian	Local								
		On Loc.								
		Local								
		On Loc.								
15	Coding Maintenance	Local								
		On Loc.								
		Local								
		On Loc.								
16	Shipping & Messengers	Local								
		On Loc.								
30	Rentals									
	Cutting Room									
	Editing Equipment									
	Projection Room									
	Music & Effects									
	Off-Line Editing									
40	Purchases									
	Supplies									
	Video Transfers									
80	Preview Expenses									
85	Additional Expenses									
95	Miscellaneous									
99	Loss, Damage, Repair									
					SUBTOTALS FROM PREVIOUS PAGE					
					SUBTOTALS THIS PAGE					
					TOTAL ACCT 5000					

A - Fringeable/Taxable   C - Non-Taxable
B - Non-Fringeable/Taxable

PROD. NO. _____   PROD. TITLE _____   DATE:_____

5100	MUSIC				SUBTOTALS		
ACCT. NO.	DESCRIPTION	TIME	RATE	AMT.	A	B	C
01	Composer						
02	Lyricist						
03	Music Coordinator						
04	Arrangers and Orchestrators						
05	Director/Conductor						
06	Copyists and Proof Readers						
07	Musicians						
08	Singers						
09	Rehearsal Pianist						
10	Coaches—Instrumental/Vocal						
11	Labor on Music Stage						
12	Labor Moving Instruments						
13	Cartage						
14	Sync Rights/Music License Fees						
15	Original Songs Purchased						
30	Rentals						
	Instruments						
	Studio—Rehearsal						
	Studio—Recording						
40	Purchases						
85	Additional Expenses						
95	Miscellaneous						
99	Loss, Damage, Repair						
				SUBTOTALS			
			TOTAL ACCT 5100				

A - Fringeable/Taxable   C - Non-Taxable
B - Non-Fringeable/Taxable

PROD. NO. _____   PROD. TITLE _____   DATE:_____

5200 FILM EFFECTS					SUBTOTALS		
ACCT. NO.	DESCRIPTION	QTY.	RATE	AMT.	A	B	C
01	Consultants						
02	Opticals						
	Fades, Dissolves, etc.						
	Special Opticals - Montages,						
	Split Screen, Computer Graphics, etc.						
	Backgrounds For Process						
03	Matte Shots (Also See Process Acct 4400)						
04	Inserts						
05	Animation						
06	Process Plates						
30	Rentals						
	Equipment						
40	Purchases						
	Film and Lab Charges						
	Materials and Supplies						
	Film - Picture Negative						
	Film - Interpositive						
	Film - Positive Print Negative						
85	Additional Expenses						
90	Sales Tax						
95	Miscellaneous						
99	Loss, Damage, Repair						
				SUBTOTALS			
			TOTAL ACCT 5200				

A - Fringeable/Taxable   C - Non-Taxable
B - Non-Fringeable/Taxable

MOVIE PRODUCTION & BUDGET FORMS... INSTANTLY!

PROD. NO. _____ PROD. TITLE _____ DATE:_____

5300 TITLES DEPARTMENT					SUBTOTALS		
ACCT. NO.	DESCRIPTION	QTY.	RATE	AMT.	A	B	C
01	Title Design						
	Art, Lettering						
02	Title Filming						
03	Sub Titles						
30	Rentals						
	Equipment						
40	Purchases						
	Film and Lab Charges						
85	Additional Expenses						
90	Sales Tax						
95	Miscellaneous						
99	Loss, Damage, Repair						
		SUBTOTALS					
		TOTAL ACCT 5300					

A - Fringeable/Taxable   C - Non-Taxable
B - Non-Fringeable/Taxable

©1984 Lone Eagle Productions, Inc.

PROD. NO. _____ PROD. TITLE _____ DATE:_____

5400 POST-PRODUCTION SOUND				SUBTOTALS		
ACCT. NO.	DESCRIPTION	TIME	RATE	AMT.	A	B	C
01	Sound Transfers — Labor/Facilities						
	Daily Reprints						
	Narration/Loops						
	Sound Effects						
	Music						
	Mix						
02	Magnetic Film						
	Narration/Loop Recording Masters						
	Narration/Loop Transfers						
	Sound Effects Recording Masters						
	Sound Effects Transfers						
	Music Recording Masters						
	Music Dub-Down Masters						
	Music Transfers						
	Dupe Work Track Transfers						
	Dubbing Masters						
	Dub Transfers						
	Music File Copy						
03	Sound Effects Recording ADR						
04	Dolby						
05	Foley						
06	Dialogue Replacement						
	Looping/Narration						
07	Vocals						
08	Music Recording						
09	Dub Downs						
10	Re-Recording (Pre-Dubbing)						
	Preview						
11	Miscellaneous Labor						
	Set Up Scoring Dubbing						
12	Sound Negative Raw Stock						
	35mm						
13	Foreign Delivery Requirements						
	Music Tracks						
14	Playback Preparation — Labor						
15	Daily Transfers — Material						
16	Reprint Transfers						
17	Playback Preparation — Material						
30	Rentals						
	Facilities (Post Production)						
40	Purchases						
85	Additional Expenses						
95	Miscellaneous						
99	Loss, Damage, Repair						
				SUBTOTALS			
			TOTAL ACCT 5400				

A - Fringeable/Taxable   C - Non-Taxable
B - Non-Fringeable/Taxable

PROD. NO. _____   **PROD. TITLE** _____   **DATE:**_____

5500	POST-PRODUCTION FILM AND LAB				SUBTOTALS		
ACCT. NO.	DESCRIPTION	QTY.	RATE	AMT.	A	B	C
01	Editorial Reprints — 1 Lite Color						
02	35mm Silent Timing Print						
03	35mm Composite Answer Print						
04	35mm Release Prints						
05	35mm Interpositive or C.R.I. (Prot. Master)						
06	35mm Internegatives						
07	1st Trial Composite Answer Print						
08	16mm Release Prints						
09	16mm Protective Master						
10	Reversal Prints Black & White						
11	35mm Sound Negative Dev. & Print						
12	16mm Sound Negative Dev. & Print						
13	Stock Footage — License Fees						
14	Stock Footage — Processing						
15	Negative Cutting						
16	Outside Lab Charges						
17	Transfer to Cassette						
18	Shipping Charges						
19	Network Requirements						
30	Rentals						
	Vault Rental						
40	Purchases						
	Picture Leader (Positive & Negative)						
	Reels						
	Cans						
	Video Cassettes						
	Videotape Dupes						
	Film Charges						
	Laboratory Charges						
85	Additional Expenses						
95	Miscellaneous						
99	Loss, Damage, Repair						
				SUBTOTALS			
				TOTAL ACCT 5500			

A - Fringeable/Taxable   C - Non-Taxable
B - Non-Fringeable/Taxable

©1984 Lone Eagle Productions, Inc.

PROD. NO. _____ PROD. TITLE _____ DATE:_____

5900 FRINGE BENEFITS AND PAYROLL TAXES—POST PRODUCTION

ACCT NO.	DESCRIPTION	PAYROLL	PENSION	HEALTH & WELFARE	TOTALS
01	DGA $ _____	% _____	% _____	% _____	
02	PGA $ _____	% _____	% _____	% _____	
03	WGA $ _____	% _____	% _____	% _____	
04	SAG $ _____	% _____	% _____	% _____	
05	IATSE $ _____	% _____	% _____	% _____	
06	NABET $ _____	% _____	% _____	% _____	
10	OTHER $ _____	% _____	% _____	% _____	
	or Allow				

SUBTOTALS

TOTAL ACCT 5900

TOTAL COSTS—POST PRODUCTION

A - Fringeable/Taxable
B - Non-Fringeable/Taxable
C - Non-Taxable

©1984 Lone Eagle Productions, Inc.

PROD. NO. _____ PROD. TITLE _____ DATE:_____

6000 PUBLICITY

ACCT. NO.	DESCRIPTION	LOCAL/ ON LOC.	DAYS/WEEKS				RATE	SUBTOTALS		
			PREP	SHOOT	WRAP	TOTAL		A	B	C
01	Publicity Firm Fee	Local								
		On Loc.								
		Local								
		On Loc.								
02	Unit Publicist	Local								
		On Loc.								
		Local								
		On Loc.								
03	Still Photographer	Local								
		On Loc.								
		Local								
		On Loc.								
04	Special Photographer	Local								
		On Loc.								
		Local								
		On Loc.								
	Additional Hire	Local								
		On Loc.								
		Local								
		On Loc.								
05	Trailers	Local								
		On Loc.								
10	Consulting Fees	Local								
		On Loc.								
		Local								
		On Loc.								
30	Rentals									
	Camera Equipment									
30	Purchases									
	Film									
	Processing									
	Prints									
	Lab Expense									
85	Additional Expenses									
	Entertainment									
95	Miscellaneous									
99	Loss, Damage, Repair									
						SUBTOTALS				
						TOTAL ACCT 6000				

A - Fringeable/Taxable
B - Non-Fringeable/Taxable
C - Non-Taxable

©1984 Lone Eagle Productions, Inc.

PROD. NO. _____ PROD. TITLE _____ DATE:_____

6100	INSURANCE		SUBTOTALS		
ACCT. NO.	DESCRIPTION	AMOUNT	A	B	C
01	Cast Insurance				
02	Negative Film Insurance				
03	Workman's Compensation Insurance				
04	Errors and Omission Insurance				
05	Faulty Raw Stock, Camera and Processing				
06	Comprehensive Liability Insurance				
07	Set, Props, and Wardrobe Insurance				
08	Extra Expense Insurance				
09	Miscellaneous Equipment Insurance				
10	Other Insurance				
	Local Insurance Requirement				
11	Medical Exams				
25	Extra Riders/Additional Insurance				
85	Additional Expenses				
95	Miscellaneous				
99	Loss, Damage, Repair				
		SUBTOTALS			
		TOTAL ACCT 6100			

© 1984 Lone Eagle Productions, Inc.

A - Fringeable/Taxable
B - Non-Fringeable/Taxable
C - Non-Taxable

PROD. NO. _____   PROD. TITLE _____

6200	GENERAL EXPENSE		SUBTOTALS		
ACCT. NO.	DESCRIPTION	RATE	A	B	C
01	Secretary				
02	Messenger Service				
03	Janitor/Cleaning Service				
04	Courtesy Payments (Also See Accts 4029 & 3717)				
05	Shipping (Also See Acct 3010)				
06	Accounting Service				
07	Production Services				
08	Entertainment				
	Meals (Also See Acct 4009)				
	Wrap Party				
09	Bank and Foreign Currency Exchange Cost				
10	Facility Sales Tax				
30	Rentals				
	Telephone & Telegraph (Also See Acct 4016)				
	Installation Charges (Also See Acct 4016)				
	Office (Also See Acct 4013)				
	Office Equip. (Also See Acct 4014)				
	Office Furniture (Also See Acct 4014)				
	Duplicating Machine (Also See Acct 4014)				
	Parking (Also See Acct 4095)				
	Data Processing				
	Storage				
40	Purchases				
	Office Supplies (Also See Acct 4012)				
	Stationery				
	Postage (Also See Acct 4011)				
	City License				
	MPAA Code Seal Fee				
85	Additional Expenses				
	Legal Fees				
	Legal Research				
	Accounting Fees				
	Preview Expenses				
90	Sales Tax				
95	Miscellaneous				
99	Loss, Damage, Repair				
		SUBTOTALS			
		TOTAL ACCT 6200			

A - Fringeable/Taxable
B - Non-Fringeable/Taxable
C - Non-Taxable

PROD. NO. _____ PROD. TITLE _____ DATE:_____

6900 FRINGE BENEFITS AND PAYROLL TAXES—OTHER COSTS

ACCT NO.	DESCRIPTION	PAYROLL	PENSION	HEALTH & WELFARE	TOTALS
01	DGA $ _____	% _____	% _____	% _____	
05	IATSE $ _____	% _____	% _____	% _____	
06	NABET $ _____	% _____	% _____	% _____	
	OTHER $ _____	% _____	% _____	% _____	
	or Allow				

SUBTOTALS				

TOTAL ACCT 6900 [   ]

TOTAL ABOVE THE LINE [   ]

TOTAL BELOW THE LINE [   ]

TOTAL POST PRODUCTION [   ]

TOTAL OTHER COSTS [   ]

TOTAL DIRECT COST [   ]

A - Fringeable/Taxable
B - Non-Fringeable/Taxable
C - Non-Taxable

©1984 Lone Eagle Productions, Inc.

PROD. NO. _____ PROD. TITLE _____ DATE:_____

7500	CONTINGENCY	
ACCT NO.	DESCRIPTION	TOTALS
01	10% x $_____ (Total Direct Cost)	
	TOTAL ACCT 7500	

7600	COMPLETION BOND (OPTIONAL)	
01	6% x $_____ (Total Direct Cost + Contingency)	
	TOTAL ACCT 7600	

7700	OVERHEAD	
01	_____% x $_____	
	TOTAL ACCT 7700	

7800	INTEREST, FINANCING CHARGES, FINDERS' FEES	
01	Interest	
02	Financing Charges	
03	Finders' Fees	
	TOTAL ACCT 7800	
	TOTAL NEGATIVE COST	

8000	DEFERMENTS	
01	DATE PAYABLE TO WHOM AMOUNT	
	TOTAL ACCT 8000	
TOTAL NEGATIVE COST (INCLUDING DEFERMENTS)		

A - Fringeable/Taxable
B - Non-Fringeable/Taxable
C - Non-Taxable

PRODUCTION FORMS

Production Forms

ACTORS
DAY OUT OF DAYS

PRODUCTION COMPANY   PRODUCTION TITLE/NUMBER   DATE

PRODUCER   DIRECTOR   PRODUCTION MANAGER./ASSISTANT DIRECTOR   SCRIPT DATE

Rehearsal-R	Hold-H	Day Number																														
Started-S	Travel-T	Date
Worked-W	Finish-F	Day of the Week
On Call-C		

No.	Character																															
		Last
1		
2		
3		
4		
5		
6		
7		
8		
9		
10		
11		
12		
13		
14		
15		
16		
17		
18		
19		
20		
21		
22		
23		
24		
25		
26		
27		
28		
29		
30		

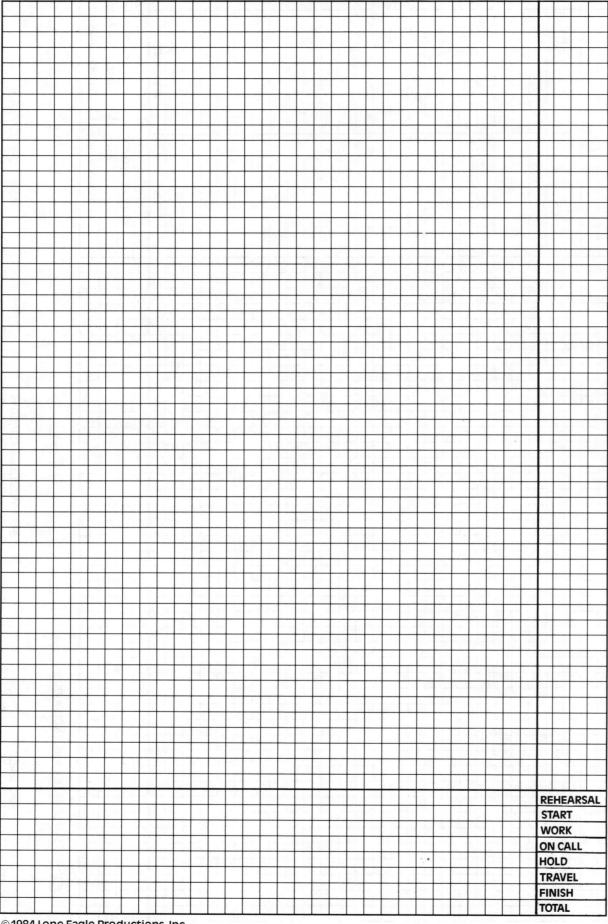

ACTORS
DAY OUT OF DAYS

REHEARSAL		
START		
WORK		
ON CALL		
HOLD		
TRAVEL		
FINISH		
TOTAL		

ACTOR'S DEAL MEMO

_____   _____   _____
PRODUCTION COMPANY   PRODUCTION TITLE / NO.   DATE

_____
ACTOR'S NAME

_____   _____
ACTOR'S ADDRESS   PHONE NO.

_____
AGENT'S NAME

_____   _____
AGENT'S ADDRESS   PHONE NO.

_____   _____
ACTOR'S PART   S.S. NO./ EMPLOYER I.D. NO.

DEAL: _____   _____   _____
                                   DAILY   WEEKLY

GUARANTEE: _____

_____

_____

_____

DETAIL: _____

_____

_____

BILLING: _____

_____

_____

_____
APPROVAL

CAST LIST

DATE

PAGE _____ OF _____

PRODUCTION COMPANY

PRODUCTION TITLE

PRODUCTION NO.

CHARACTER	NAME AND ADDRESS	TELEPHONE NO.

PRODUCTION TITLE: _____ **NO.** _____ **DATE:** _____

CAST MEMBER	SCENE NUMBER(S)

©1984 Lone Eagle Productions, Inc.

CONTACT LIST
TOP SHEET

_____
DATE

_____   _____   _____
PRODUCTION COMPANY   PRODUCTION TITLE   PRODUCTION NO.

CONTACT	PAGE NO.	CONTACT	PAGE NO.	CONTACT	PAGE NO.
Airlines		Equipment		Office Supplies	
Airport		Film/Raw Stock		Pharmacy	
Art Supplies		Fire Dept.		Photography	
Ambulance		Florist		Police	
Bank		Food/Coffee/Water/Liquor		Payroll	
Beepers		Furniture Rental		Post Office	
Camera		Hardware		Prop Supplies	
Casting		Hospital		Production Office	
Cleaners		Hotels		Restaurants	
Copier/Dupe/Printing		Insurance		Studios	
Construction		Lumber Supplies		Telephone	
Custom Brokers		Mayor's Office of Film		Transportation	
Dailies/Lab		Messenger		Walkie-Talkies	
Dentist		Office Machines		Wardrobe	
Doctor		Office Maintenance		Weather	
Editorial					

CONTACT LIST

PAGE _____ OF _____

PRODUCTION TITLE: _____

DATE: _____

AREA	CONTACT	TELEPHONE NO.

©1984 Lone Eagle Productions, Inc.

CREW DEAL MEMO

_____   _____   _____
PRODUCTION COMPANY   PRODUCTION TITLE / NO.   DATE

_____
EMPLOYEE NAME

_____
EMPLOYEE ADDRESS

_____   _____   _____
POSITION   S.S. NO./EMPLOYER I.D. NO.   UNION/GUILD

DEAL: _____

_____

_____

_____

_____

_____

_____

_____

_____

_____

_____

_____

_____

ACCEPTED BY: **APPROVED BY:**

_____   _____
EMPLOYEE'S SIGNATURE   EXECUTIVE IN CHARGE OF PRODUCTION

CREW LIST

DATE _____

PRODUCTION COMPANY _____   PRODUCTION TITLE _____   PRODUCTION NO.

POSITION	NAME AND ADDRESS	TELEPHONE NO.

CREW MOVEMENT LIST

DAY OF THE WEEK	DATE	MOVEMENT INFORMATION — EXAMPLE: AIRLINE INFO; BUS; ETC. — INSTRUCTIONS	
		CREW MEMBERS NAME	**POSITION**
		COMMENTS	

DAY OF THE WEEK	DATE	MOVEMENT INFORMATION — EXAMPLE: AIRLINE INFO; BUS; ETC. — INSTRUCTIONS	
		CREW MEMBERS NAME	**POSITION**
		COMMENTS	

DAY OF THE WEEK	DATE	MOVEMENT INFORMATION — EXAMPLE: AIRLINE INFO; BUS; ETC. — INSTRUCTIONS	
		CREW MEMBERS NAME	**POSITION**
		COMMENTS	

DAILY CALL SHEET

PRODUCTION COMPANY/PHONE NO.	PRODUCTION TITLE	PRODUCTION NUMBER

DAY / DATE	DAY NUMBER	CREW CALL

DIRECTOR	1ST ASSISTANT DIRECTOR	2ND ASSISTANT DIRECTOR

CAST	CHARACTER	MAKE-UP	ON SET	TRANSPORT

EXTRAS AND STANDINS		PROPS		SPECIAL INSTRUCTIONS

SET NAME/ACTOR NO.	SCENES	PAGES	D/N	LOCATION

ADVANCE SCHEDULE	TRANSPORTATION

COVER SET	

DAILY CALL SHEET—(Cont'd)

CREW CALL

Director _____	Set Grips _____	V.T.R. Crew _____	Trans. Coord. _____	**Vehicles:**
Choreographer _____	Rig Grips _____	Sound Mixer _____	Trans. Capt. _____	Camera Cars _____
Dialogue Coach _____	Crane Grips _____	Boom Oper. _____	Drivers _____	Sound Wagon _____
Stunt Coord. _____	Constr. Grips _____	Cable Men _____	Editor _____	Camera Truck _____
1st Asst. Dir. _____	Scenic Grips _____	Playback _____	Asst. Editor _____	Electric Trucks _____
2nd Asst. Dir. _____	Scenic Chargeman _____	Gaffer _____	Coffee _____	Grip Trucks _____
D.G.A. Trainee _____	Scenic Artists _____	Set Elect. _____	Caterer _____	Prop Trucks _____
P.A.'s _____	Set Standby Scenic _____	Rig Elect. _____		Genny Trucks _____
Script Super _____	Greensmen _____	Genny Oper. _____	**Equipment:**	Wardrobe Truck _____
Loc. Mgr. _____	Watchmen _____	Spec. Efx. _____	Cameras _____	Add'l Trucks _____
Prod. Auditor _____	Police _____	Set Dec. _____	Zooms _____	Buses _____
Tech. Advisor _____	Firemen _____	Leadman _____	Booms _____	Station Wagons _____
Prod. Designer _____	First Aid/Nurse _____	Swing Gang _____	Dollies _____	Cars _____
Art Director _____	Doctor _____	Wranglers _____	Cranes _____	Vans _____
Set Designer _____	Dir. of Photo. _____	Costume Des. _____	Sound Channels _____	People Mover _____
Sketch Artist _____	Camera Op. _____	Wardrobe _____	Playback/PA _____	Picture Cars _____
Const. Coord. _____	1st Asst. Cam. _____	Make-up _____	Projector _____	Trailers _____
Carpenters _____	2nd Asst. Cam. _____	Hair Dressers _____	Arc Lamps _____	Portable Toilets _____
Propmakers _____	Camera Trainee _____	Prop Master _____	Special Props _____	Honey Wagon _____
Set Standby Carp. _____	Still Camera _____	Asst. Props _____	Meals _____	
Key Grip _____	Projectionist _____	Outside Props _____	Portable Genny _____	

Notes:

DAILY PRODUCTION REPORT

PRODUCTION COMPANY　　　　PRODUCTION TITLE　　　　PRODUCTION NUMBER

DAY / DATE　　　　SHOOTING DAY NUMBER　　　　CREW CALL

1st SHOT　　　　LAST SHOT OF DAY　　　　CREW WRAP

1st SHOT AFTER LUNCH　　　　DIRECTOR　　　　START DATE

PRODUCER　　　　ESTIMATED FINISH DATE

PRODUCTION DAYS	SCHED. DAYS	ACTUAL DAYS	SCRIPT LOG		PAGES	SCENES	ADDED SCENES	RETAKEN SCENES	
LOCAL LOCATIONS			SCRIPT TOTAL						**SCRIPT NOTES**
REHEARSAL DAYS			SHOT BEFORE						
STUDIO DAYS			SHOT TODAY						
L. LOCATION DAYS			TOTAL SHOT TO DATE						
HOLIDAYS			MINUTES SHOT	BEFORE TODAY	TO DATE	SCENE NOS.		SOUND NOS.	
IDLE DAYS									
								ADDED/RETAKES	

		FILM					STILLS	SOUND	
		DRAWN	EXPOSED	PRINT	N.G.	WASTE	35 MM STILLS	NO. 1/4" ROLLS	WILD-TRAX
DISTANT LOCATIONS	BEFORE								
REHEARSAL DAYS									
LOCATION DAYS	TODAY								
HOLIDAYS									
IDLE DAYS									
TRAVEL	TO DATE								

TOTAL DAYS AHEAD OR BEHIND SCHEDULE		TOTAL SHOT INVENTORY		MEALS	1ST	2ND	3RD	PENALTIES	

SCENE NAME	LOCATION

REMARKS

ASSISTANT DIRECTOR　　　　WEATHER　　　　PRODUCTION MANAGER　　**(OVER)**

DAILY PRODUCTION REPORT—(Cont'd)

CAST MEMBERS				STATUS												
REHEARSE - R STARTED - S HOLD - H	TRAVEL - T WORKED - W	ON CALL - C FINISHED - F	W S R	H F C	TIME CALLED		MEALS	TRAVEL TIME	DIS-MISSED	HOURS			DAYS		
					MAKE-UP WARD.	ON SET				ST.	1½	DBL.	WKD.	IDLE	TOTAL
EXTRAS/STAND INS:															

CREW CALL

Director _____	Set Grips _____	V.T.R. Crew _____	Trans. Coord. _____	**Vehicles:**
Choreographer _____	Rig Grips _____	Sound Mixer _____	Trans. Capt. _____	Camera Cars _____
Dialogue Coach _____	Crane Grips _____	Boom Oper. _____	Drivers _____	Sound Wagon _____
Stunt Coord. _____	Constr. Grips _____	Cable Men _____	Editor _____	Camera Truck _____
1st Asst. Dir. _____	Scenic Grips _____	Playback _____	Asst. Editor _____	Electric Trucks _____
2nd Asst. Dir. _____	Scenic Chargeman ___	Gaffer _____	Coffee _____	Grip Trucks _____
D.G.A. Trainee _____	Scenic Artists _____	Set Elect. _____	Caterer _____	Prop Trucks _____
P.A.'s _____	Set Standby Scenic ___	Rig Elect. _____		Genny Trucks _____
Script Super _____	Greensmen _____	Genny Oper. _____	**Equipment:**	Wardrobe Truck _____
Loc. Mgr. _____	Watchmen _____	Spec. Efx. _____	Cameras _____	Add'l Trucks _____
Prod. Auditor _____	Police _____	Set Dec. _____	Zooms _____	Buses _____
Tech. Advisor _____	Firemen _____	Leadman _____	Booms _____	Station Wagons _____
Prod. Designer _____	First Aid/Nurse _____	Swing Gang _____	Dollies _____	Cars _____
Art Director _____	Doctor _____	Wranglers _____	Cranes _____	Vans _____
Set Designer _____	Dir. of Photo. _____	Costume Des. _____	Sound Channels _____	People Mover _____
Sketch Artist _____	Camera Op. _____	Wardrobe _____	Playback/PA _____	Picture Cars _____
Const. Coord. _____	1st Asst. Cam. _____	Make-up _____	Projector _____	Trailers _____
Carpenters _____	2nd Asst. Cam. _____	Hair Dressers _____	Arc Lamps _____	Portable Toilets _____
Propmakers _____	Camera Trainee _____	Prop Master _____	Special Props _____	Honey Wagon _____
Set Standby Carp. _____	Still Camera _____	Asst. Props _____	Meals _____	
Key Grip _____	Projectionist _____	Outside Props _____	Portable Genny _____	

Notes:

DEVELOPMENT COSTS

_____
DATE

_____
PRODUCTION COMPANY

_____
PRODUCTION TITLE/NO.

_____
PRODUCER

_____
DIRECTOR

ACCOUNT NO.	ACCOUNT NAME/DESCRIPTION		AMOUNT ($)
_____	Story		$ _____
_____	Screenplay		$ _____
_____	Script Preparation		
_____	Typing	$ _____	
_____	Duplication	$ _____	$ _____
_____	Budget Preparation		
_____	Script Breakdown &		
_____	Production Board		$ _____
_____	Accounting		$ _____
_____	Legal		
_____	Incorporation	$ _____	
_____	Contracts	$ _____	
_____	Other	$ _____	$ _____
_____	Travel & Entertainment		$ _____
_____	Office Overhead		$ _____
_____	Additional Expenses		$ _____
_____	Miscellaneous		$ _____
		Total	$ _____

EQUIPMENT RENTAL AGREEMENT

_____   _____   _____
PRODUCTION COMPANY   PRODUCTION TITLE / NO.   DATE

_____   _____   _____
RENTING COMPANY

_____   _____   _____
                             COMPANY ADDRESS   PHONE NO.

_____   _____
EMPLOYEE NAME

_____   _____
                             EMPLOYEE ADDRESS

_____   _____
POSITION   S.S. NO./EMPLOYER I.D. NO.

_____
_____
_____
_____
_____
_____

EQUIPMENT

I, _____ , warrant that I am the owner of the above described
equipment and that I have the right and/or authority to rent or lease same
to _____ , and/or the Producer, Production
entitled _____ .

Daily Rate/or Weekly Rate of _____ beginning on _____ delivered
to _____ premises on _____ (Date).

I understand and agree that _____ , and/or
the Producer shall have no responsibility or liability for the safekeeping of the equipment nor shall they be responsible or liable for the replacement of the equipment
or any part thereof.

_____   _____
RENTER'S SIGNATURE   APPROVAL

LOANOUT AGREEMENT

PRODUCTION COMPANY	PRODUCTION TITLE / NO.	DATE

LENDING COMPANY		

	COMPANY ADDRESS	PHONE NO.

EMPLOYEE NAME		

	EMPLOYEE ADDRESS	

POSITION	S.S. NO./EMPLOYER I.D. NO.	UNION / GUILD

DEAL:

_____

_____

_____

_____

_____

_____

_____

_____

_____

_____

Lending Corp. represents and warrants that it is a California corporation in good standing entitled to furnish all of the services of Employee to be furnished hereunder, that it is authorized to enter into this agreement, that it is a signatory to the Union or Guild agreement referred to above (and that Employee is a member in good standing of such Union or Guild), and that the foregoing shall remain so during the term of this agreement.

ACCEPTED: APPROVED:

By _____   _____
Its _____   EXECUTIVE IN CHARGE OF PRODUCTION

The undersigned hereby acknowledges that he has read and is familiar with, and that he hereby endorses and approves, all of the provisions of the foregoing agreement and agrees to be bound thereby and to perform all of the terms and conditions thereof, insofar as the same are to be performed by him, in the same manner as if he had executed said agreement; and that he will look solely to Lending Corp. for all payments which may be due him under said agreement.

_____
EMPLOYEE'S SIGNATURE

PRODUCTION TITLE _____ Date _____

LOCATION CREW CHECK LIST

TITLE	YES	NO	PER DIEM	HOTEL	MEALS	REMARKS
Executive Producer						
Producer						
Associate Producer						
Producer's Secretary						
Director						
Second Unit Director						
Choreographer						
Dialogue Director						
Director's Secretary						
Cast Members						
Casting Director						
Welfare Worker/Teacher						
Stunt Coordinator						
Production Manager						
First Assistant Director						
Second Assistant Director						
Location Manager						
Production Accountant						
Assistant to Prod. Acct.						
DGA Trainee						
Production Assistants						
Script Supervisor						
Production Office Coordinator						
Production Secretary						
Technical Advisor						
Extra Casting Director						
Production Designer						
Art Director						
Assistant Art Director						
Set Designer						
Draftsman						
Sketch Artist						
Construction Coordinator						
Construction Foreman						
Set Decorator						
Swing Gang — Leadman						

  (Continued on Next Page)

PRODUCTION TITLE _____   Date _____

LOCATION CREW CHECK LIST

TITLE	YES	NO	PER DIEM	HOTEL	MEALS	REMARKS
Swing Gang—Second						
Greensman						
Painter						
Propmaster						
Asst. Propmaster						
Special Effects Foreman						
Special Effects—Add'l						
Director of Photography						
Camera Operator						
Additional Camera Operator						
1st Assistant Camera						
2nd Assistant Camera						
Special Camera Operator						
Camera Trainee						
Mixer						
Mike Boom Operator						
Cable Puller						
Key Grip						
2nd Company Grip						
Dolly Grip						
Crane Grip						
Company Grip						
Gaffer						
Best Boy						
Generator Operator						
Electricians						
Costume Designer						
Assistant to Costume Designer						
Women's Costumer						
Women's Costumer—Set						
Men's Costumer						
Men's Costumer—Set						
Tailor						
Seamstress						
Make-up Artist						
Make-up Assistant						
Body Make-up						
Hair Stylist						
Hair Stylist Assistant						
Transportation Coordinator						
Captain						
Co-Captain						
Drivers						

(Continued on Next Page)

PRODUCTION TITLE _____   Date _____

LOCATION CREW CHECK LIST

TITLE	YES	NO	PER DIEM	HOTEL	MEALS	REMARKS
Editor						
Assistant Editor						
Video Tape Cameraman						
Video Monitor Operators						
Unit Publicist						
Still Photographer						

MEAL ALLOWANCE SHEET

DAY / DATE _____

PRODUCTION TITLE _____

PRODUCTION NO. _____

DEPARTMENT _____

MEAL RATES
Breakfast _____
Lunch _____
Dinner _____

DAY	MON			TUE			WED			THU			FRI			SAT			SUN			TOTAL	NAME	SIGNATURE
DATE	B	L /	D	B	L /	D	B	L /	D	B	L /	D	B	L /	D	B	L /	D	B	L /	D			
TOTAL																									

PRODUCTION MANAGER _____

APPROVAL _____

LOCATION AUDITOR _____

© 1984 Lone Eagle Productions, Inc.

ONE LINE SHOOTING SCHEDULE

PRODUCTION COMPANY _____ PRODUCTION TITLE _____ PRODUCTION NUMBER _____

PRODUCER _____ DIRECTOR _____ DATE _____

DAY NO.	DAY/ DATE	INT/ EXT	SET NAME/ ONE LINE DESCRIPTION	D/N	SCENE NO.	TOTAL PAGES

MOVIE PRODUCTION & BUDGET FORMS . . . INSTANTLY!

PER DIEM EXPENSE REPORT

PRODUCTION COMPANY   PRODUCTION TITLE/NO.   DATE

EMPLOYEE NAME   S.S. NO.   UNION/GUILD

DAY:	MONDAY		TUESDAY		WEDNESDAY		THURSDAY		FRIDAY		SATURDAY		SUNDAY		TOTAL
DATE:															
Transportation: Tickets															
Local (taxi, carfare, etc.)															
Baggage handling															
Room															
Meals: Breakfast															
Lunch															
Dinner															
Telephone															
Laundry															
Other															
TOTAL															
DAILY ALLOWANCE (if any)															
"TOTAL" Less "DAILY ALLOWANCE"															

EMPLOYEE'S SIGNATURE   APPROVAL

© 1984 Lone Eagle Productions, Inc.

PETTY CASH ADVANCE RECEIPT

_____   _____   _____
PRODUCTION COMPANY   PRODUCTION TITLE / NO.   DATE

_____   _____   _____
EMPLOYEE'S NAME   DEPARTMENT   AMOUNT

_____ **DOLLARS**
(WRITE IN AMOUNT)

PURPOSE _____

_____

I hereby acknowledge receipt of said sum and hereby agree to provide receipts to document expenditures. I also hereby grant the Production Company authority to deduct any undocumented expenditures from my last pay check.

_____   _____   _____
EMPLOYEE'S SIGNATURE   APPROVED   PAYMENT RECEIVED

©1984 Lone Eagle Productions, Inc.

PETTY CASH ADVANCE RECEIPT

_____   _____   _____
PRODUCTION COMPANY   PRODUCTION TITLE / NO.   DATE

_____   _____   _____
EMPLOYEE'S NAME   DEPARTMENT   AMOUNT

_____ **DOLLARS**
(WRITE IN AMOUNT)

PURPOSE _____

_____

I hereby acknowledge receipt of said sum and hereby agree to provide receipts to document expenditures. I also hereby grant the Production Company authority to deduct any undocumented expenditures from my last pay check.

_____   _____   _____
EMPLOYEE'S SIGNATURE   APPROVED   PAYMENT RECEIVED

©1984 Lone Eagle Productions, Inc.

PETTY CASH—EXPENSE REPORT

PRODUCTION COMPANY	PRODUCTION TITLE	PRODUCTION NUMBER
EMPLOYEE NAME	DEPARTMENT	VOUCHER NUMBER

FROM _____ 19 _____ TO _____ 19 _____ PAID BY CHECK NO. _____

ENTERED	AUDITED	APPROVED	PAID

DATE	NO.	DESCRIPTION/PAYEE	PURPOSE	ACCT.	AMOUNT

PETTY CASH ADVANCE RECEIVED	$_____	RECEIPTS PAID	$_____
TOTAL RECEIPTS AND CASH	$_____	CASH ON HAND	$_____
(OVER OR UNDER)	$_____	TOTAL	$_____

DISTRIBUTION OF EXPENSES

												MISCELLANEOUS
												TOTALS

PETTY CASH REIMBURSEMENT RECEIPT

PRODUCTION COMPANY	PRODUCTION TITLE/NO.	DATE
EMPLOYEE'S NAME	DEPARTMENT	AMOUNT

_____ DOLLARS
(WRITE IN AMOUNT)

EXPENSE REPORT DATED _____

EMPLOYEE'S SIGNATURE	APPROVED	PAYMENT RECEIVED

©1984 Lone Eagle Productions, Inc.

PETTY CASH REIMBURSEMENT RECEIPT

PRODUCTION COMPANY	PRODUCTION TITLE/NO.	DATE
EMPLOYEE'S NAME	DEPARTMENT	AMOUNT

_____ DOLLARS
(WRITE IN AMOUNT)

EXPENSE REPORT DATED _____

EMPLOYEE'S SIGNATURE	APPROVED	PAYMENT RECEIVED

©1984 Lone Eagle Productions, Inc.

PHOTO RELEASE

PRODUCTION COMPANY	PRODUCTION TITLE/NO.	DATE

I hereby give and grant to you the right to use my name and/or the right to photograph my physical likeness in any manner you desire and/or the right to reproduce and record my voice and other sound effects made by me, and I hereby consent to the use of my name and/or said photographs, likenesses and any reproductions thereof and/or the recordations and reproductions of my voice and other sound effects, by you, your licensees, successors and assigns, in or in connection with the production, exhibition, distribution, advertising and exploitation and/or other use of any of your photoplays and/or otherwise.

NAME	SIGNATURE	ADDRESS

PRODUCERS BUDGETARY
TOP SHEET

DATE: _____

_____	_____	_____
PRODUCTION COMPANY	PRODUCTION TITLE	PRODUCTION NO.
_____	_____	_____
PRODUCER	DIRECTOR	SCRIPT DATE
_____	_____	_____
START DATE	FINISH DATE	ANSWER PRINT DATE

SHOOTING SCHEDULE	FIRST UNIT	SECOND UNIT
LOCAL LOCATION		
Rehearsal Days		
Studio Days		
Local Location Days		
Holidays		
Idle Days		
Travel Days		
DISTANT LOCATION		
Rehearsal Days		
Location Days		
Holidays		
Idle Days		
Travel Days		
TOTAL DAYS		

_____
TOTAL BUDGET

APPROVED BY:

_____   _____
PRODUCER   DIRECTOR

PRODUCTION COMPANY _____ PRODUCTION TITLE/NO. _____ PERIOD ENDING _____

ACCT. NO.	ACCOUNT NAME	ORIGINAL BUDGET	TO DATE	ESTIMATED COST TO COMPLETE	ESTIMATED FINAL COST	(OVER) UNDER BUDGET	COMMENTS
1000	Story and Screenplay						
1100	Producers Unit						
1200	Directors Unit						
1300	Cast Unit						
1400	Travel and Living Unit						
1900	Fringe Benefits & Payroll Taxes						
TOTAL ABOVE THE LINE BUDGET							
2000	Production Department						
2100	Extra Talent						
2200	Art Department						
2300	Set Construction						
2400	Set Dressing						
2500	Property						
2600	Picture Vehicles						
2700	Special Effects						
2800	Camera						

(Continued on Next Page)

PRODUCTION COST REPORT

PRODUCTION COMPANY _____

PRODUCTION TITLE/NO. _____

PERIOD ENDING _____

ACCT. NO.	ACCOUNT NAME	ORIGINAL BUDGET	TO DATE	ESTIMATED COST TO COMPLETE	ESTIMATED FINAL COST	(OVER) UNDER BUDGET	COMMENTS
3000	Special Equipment						
3100	Sound						
3200	Grip						
3300	Lighting						
3400	Wardrobe						
3500	Make-up and Hair						
3600	Set Operations						
3700	Site Rental						
3800	Stage Expense						
4000	Location Expense						
4100	Second Unit						
4200	Tests						

(Continued on Next Page)

PRODUCTION COST REPORT

PRODUCTION COMPANY _____ PRODUCTION TITLE/NO. _____ PERIOD ENDING _____

ACCT. NO.	ACCOUNT NAME	ORIGINAL BUDGET	TO DATE	ESTIMATED COST TO COMPLETE	ESTIMATED FINAL COST	(OVER) UNDER BUDGET	COMMENTS
4300	Miniatures						
4400	Process						
4500	Animals						
4600	Transportation						
4700	Rawstock/Laboratory						
4900	Fringe Benefits & Payroll Taxes						
TOTAL BELOW THE LINE BUDGET							
5000	Film Editing						
5100	Music						
5200	Film Effects						
5300	Titles						
5400	Post Production Sound						
5500	Post Production Film						
5900	Fringe Benefits & Payroll Taxes						
TOTAL POST PRODUCTION BUDGET							

(Continued on Next Page)

PRODUCTION COST REPORT

PRODUCTION COMPANY

PRODUCTION TITLE/NO.

PERIOD ENDING

ACCT. NO.	ACCOUNT NAME	ORIGINAL BUDGET	TO DATE	ESTIMATED COST TO COMPLETE	ESTIMATED FINAL COST	(OVER) UNDER BUDGET	COMMENTS
6000	Publicity						
6100	Insurance						
6200	General Expense						
6900	Fringe Benefits & Payroll Taxes						
	TOTAL OTHER COSTS						
	TOTAL DIRECT COSTS						
7500	Contingency						
7600	Completion Bond						
7700	Overhead						
7800	Interest						
	TOTAL NEGATIVE COSTS						
8000	Deferments						
	TOTAL NEGATIVE COSTS (incl. Deferments)						

PRODUCTION CHECKLIST   DATE: _____

CAST—SPEAKING	
Deal Memos	
Contracts Signed	
Wardrobe Fitted	
Special Make-up	
Hair Falls or Wigs	
Stunt/Photo Doubles	
Minors—Intent to Employ	
Welfare Worker/Teacher	
SAG—Station 12 Checked	
Musicians	
Other:	

CREW—CAMERA	
Equipment Ordered/Checked	
Film Ordered	
Dolly Needed	
Other:	

CREW—SOUND	
Equipment Ordered/Checked	
1/4" Tape Ordered	
Walkie Talkies	
PA System	
Playback	
Communication System to Set	
Other:	

CREW—OTHER	
Art Director—	
Grips—Any Special Equipment	
Electricians—Light Changes	
Special Effects—Discuss & Set	
Props—Discuss	
Make-up—Period/Special	
Body Make-up	
Hair—Period/Special	
Wardrobe—Period/Special	
Greensman—Special	
Script Supervisor—Script Timing	
Dialogue Coach	
Transportation Coordinator—Period/Special	
Set Decorator—Period/Special	
Other:	

SILENT—ATMOSPHERE	
Interviews	
Fittings	
Vouchers	
Mileage	
Minors—Intent to Employ	
Welfare Worker/Teacher	
Make-up or Hair—Period/Special	
Adjustments Necessary	
Piano Player for Music Cues	
Other:	

MISCELLANEOUS	
Technical Advisors	
First Aid	
Police	
Guards	
Firemen & Fire Permits	
City License/Permits	
Location Permits	
Heaters	
Livestock or Animals	
Handlers or Wranglers	
Tables and Benches	
Schoolroom Facilities	
Coffee & Rolls	
Breakfast	
Lunch	
Dinner	
Call Sheets	
Set Status Reports	
Production Reports	
Transportation and Lunch Lists	
Other:	

EQUIPMENT	
Generator	
Extra Camera	
Crane	
Special Process	
Trucks	
Vehicles—Picture or Standby	
Buses	
Insert Car	
Water Wagon	
Honeywagons	
Dressing Rooms	
Motor Homes	
Other:	

PRODUCTION REPORT SUMMARY
TOP SHEET

PRODUCTION COMPANY   PRODUCTION TITLE   PRODUCTION NO.

SHOOTING DAY/DATE   SHOOTING DAY NO.   CREW CALL

1ST SHOT OF DAY   LAST SHOT OF DAY   CREW WRAP

	SETUPS	SCENES	MINUTES	PAGES
PREVIOUS				
TODAY				
TOTAL				

LOCATIONS COMPLETED TODAY

SCENES COMPLETED TODAY

ACTORS WORKED

FINAL COMMENTS

©1984 Lone Eagle Productions, Inc.

PRODUCTION GRATUITIES FORM

PRODUCTION TITLE _____ NO. _____ DATE _____

DATE	ITEM	AMOUNT

SCRIPT
BREAKDOWN SHEET

DATE
_____

PRODUCTION COMPANY
_____

PRODUCTION TITLE/NO.
_____

BREAKDOWN PAGE NO.
_____

SCENE NO.
_____

SCENE NAME
_____

INT. OR EXT.
_____

DESCRIPTION
_____

DAY OR NIGHT
_____

PAGE COUNT
_____

CAST Red (1301-2-3)	**STUNTS** Orange (1304 - 5)	**EXTRAS/ATMOSPHERE** Green (2120)
	EXTRAS/SILENT BITS Yellow (2120)	
SPECIAL EFFECTS Blue (2700)	**PROPS** Violet (2500)	**VEHICLES/ANIMALS** Pink (2600/4500)
WARDROBE Circle (3400)	**MAKE-UP/HAIR** Asterisk (3500)	**SOUND EFFECTS/MUSIC** Brown (5100,5300,5400)
SPECIAL EQUIPMENT Box	**PRODUCTION NOTES**	

SCRIPT SUPERVISOR'S REPORT

SERIES: _____ PROD. NO.: _____

TITLE: _____ DATE: _____

SHOOTING DAY: _____ CREW CALL: _____

1ST SHOT A.M.: _____ LUNCH _____ TILL _____

1ST SHOT P.M.: _____ DINNER _____ TILL _____

LAST SHOT: _____ WRAP: _____

SCENES TODAY: _____

ADDED SCENES: _____

RETAKES: _____

	SCENES	PAGES	MINUTES	SETUPS	ADDED SCENES	RETAKES
In Script						
Taken Previously						
Taken Today						
Taken To Date						
To Be Taken						

REMARKS: _____

_____

SCRIPT SUPERVISOR'S SIGNATURE: _____

SCRIPT SUPERVISOR'S REPORT

SERIES: _____ PROD. NO.: _____

TITLE: _____ DATE: _____

SHOOTING DAY: _____ CREW CALL: _____

1ST SHOT A.M.: _____ LUNCH _____ TILL _____

1ST SHOT P.M.: _____ DINNER _____ TILL _____

LAST SHOT: _____ WRAP: _____

SCENES TODAY: _____

ADDED SCENES: _____

RETAKES: _____

	SCENES	PAGES	MINUTES	SETUPS	ADDED SCENES	RETAKES
In Script						
Taken Previously						
Taken Today						
Taken To Date						
To Be Taken						

REMARKS: _____

_____

SCRIPT SUPERVISOR'S SIGNATURE: _____

SET STATUS REPORT

PRODUCTION COMPANY   PRODUCTION TITLE/NO.   DAY/DATE

CREW CALL: DINNER:
1ST SHOT: 1ST SHOT:
LUNCH: FINISH:
1ST SHOT: OUT:

REPORT NO.	TIME	SCENE NO.	SETUPS COMPLETED	SCENE/NAME/REMARKS

STUNT BREAKDOWN FORM

_____	_____	_____
PRODUCTION COMPANY	PRODUCTION TITLE	PRODUCTION NO.
_____	_____	_____
PRODUCER	DIRECTOR	PRODUCTION MGR.
_____	_____	_____
STUNT COORDINATOR	SCRIPT DATE	DATE

SCENE NAME(S) _____

SCENE NO.(S) _____

SCENE DESCRIPTION _____

_____

_____

_____

_____

_____

CAST/STUNT PERSON _____

_____

_____

_____

_____

EQUIPMENT DESCRIPTION _____ **PROVIDED BY** _____

_____

_____

_____

_____

_____

RIGGING _____

_____

_____

UNIT PRODUCTION MANAGER AND ASSISTANT DIRECTOR
DEAL MEMORANDUM

This confirms our agreement to employ you on the film project described below as follows:

_____   _____
NAME   S.S. NO./EMPLOYER I.D. NO.

_____   _____
ADDRESS   TELEPHONE

_____

☐ UNIT PRODUCTION MANAGER
☐ FIRST ASSISTANT DIRECTOR
☐ SECOND ASSISTANT DIRECTOR
☐ ADDITIONAL SECOND ASSISTANT DIRECTOR

☐ THEATRICAL MOTION PICTURE
☐ TELEVISION MOTION PICTURE

TITLE: _____

SALARY: _____ ☐ per week ☐ per day

START DATE: _____

GUARANTEED PERIOD: _____ ☐ week(s) ☐ day(s)

       and shall be prorated thereafter.

PRODUCTION FEE: _____

☐ STUDIO   ☐ DISTANT LOCATION   ☐ COMBINATION

The undersigned reserves the right to terminate the employee at any time, subject only to the obligation to pay the balance of any compensation due, pursuant to Sections 7-1403, 13-206 and other applicable provisions of the DGA Basic Agreement of 1978, to which this employment is subject.

_____
Signatory Company

DATE: _____   _____
                           By

WORLD TIME CHART

Add or subtract number of hours to Los Angeles time—Standard/Daylight		
Argentina +5/ +4	Holland +9/ +8	Phillipines +16/ +15
Australia +19[a]/ +17	India +13½/ +12½	Portugal +8[f]/ +8[g]
Austria +9/ +8	Indonesia +15/ +14	Puerto Rico +4/ +3
Belgium +9/ +8	Iran +11½/ +10½	Singapore +15½/ +14½
Brazil +5/ +4	Iraq +11/ +10	South Africa +10/ +9
Burma +14½/ +13½	Ireland +8/ +8	Spain +10/ +9
Chile +4/ +3	Israel +10/ +9	Sweden +9/ +8
Columbia +3/ +2	Italy +9/ +8[d]	Switzerland +9/ +8
Denmark +9/ +8	Japan +17/ +16	Taiwan +16/ +16
Dominican Republic +3/ +3	Lebanon +10/ +9	Thailand +15/ +14
Ecuador +3/ +2	Malaysia +15½/ +14½	Trinidad +4/ +3
Egypt +10/ +10[b]	Mexico +2/ +1	Uruguay +5/ +4
Finland +10/ +9	New Zealand +21[e]/ +19	Venezuela +4/ +3
France +9/ +8	Norway +9/ +8	Vietnam +16/ +15
Germany +9/ +8	Pakistan +13/ +12	
Great Britain +8/ +8	Panama +3/ +2	
Greece +10/ +10[c]	Paraguay +4/ +3	
Hong Kong +16/ +16	Peru +3/ +2	

Daylight Savings Time = last Sunday in April — last Sunday in October

a = +18 — 1st Sun/March — last Sun/April
b = +9 — last Sun/Sept. — last Sun/Oct.
c = +9 — 2nd Sun/Sept. — last Sun/Oct.
d = +9 — 1st Sun/June — last Sun/Sept.
e = +20 — 1st Sun/March — last Sun/April
f = +9 — last Sun/March— last Sun/April
g = +7 — last Sun/Sept. — last Sun/Oct.

ORDER FORM

DIRECTORIES

		Price	*CA Tax	Total
_____	FILM DISTRIBUTION GUIDE Volume 1	125.00	10.31	_____
_____	FILM DIRECTORS 10th Edition	50.00	4.13	_____
_____	FILM PRODUCERS, STUDIOS, AGENTS & CASTING DIRECTORS 4th Edition	45.00	371	_____
_____	CINEMATOGRAPHERS, PRODUCTION DESIGNERS, COSTUME DESIGNERS & FILM EDITORS 4th Edition	45.00	3.71	_____
_____	SPECIAL FX & STUNTS 2nd Edition	39.95	3.30	_____
_____	FILM WRITERS 5th Edition—*available September 1994*	50.00	4.13	_____
_____	FILM ACTORS 2nd Edition—*available August 1994*	50.00	4.13	_____
_____	FILM COMPOSERS 2nd Edition	45.00	3.71	_____
_____	TV WRITERS 3rd Edition	45.00	3.71	_____
_____	TV DIRECTORS 2nd Edition	40.00	3.30	_____

BOOKS

		Price	*CA Tax	Total
_____	FUNNY BUSINESS: The Craft of Comedy Writing	18.95	1.56	_____
_____	FILM SCHEDULING	19.95	1.65	_____
_____	FILM SCHEDULING/BUDGETING WORKBOOK	19.95	1.65	_____
_____	MOVIE PRODUCTION & BUDGET FORMS	19.95	1.65	_____
_____	FILM EDITING ROOM HANDBOOK	22.95	1.89	_____
_____	SCREEN ACTING	15.95	1.32	_____
_____	FILMMAKER'S DICTIONARY	12.95	1.07	_____
_____	THE LANGUAGE OF VISUAL EFFECTS	18.95	1.56	_____
_____	THE HOLLYWOOD JOBHUNTER'S SURVIVAL GUIDE	16.95	1.40	_____
_____	SILENT PICTURES	9.95	.82	_____
_____	TOP SECRETS: SCREENWRITING	19.95	1.65	_____
_____	THE COMPLETE FILM PRODUCTION HANDBOOK	34.95	2.88	_____
_____	THE GLAM SCAM	13.95	1.15	_____
_____	FILM BUDGETING —*available Summer 1994*	22.95	1.89	_____

SOFTWARE

		Price—*CA Tax
_____	COLLABORATOR	329.00 • 27.14
_____	FINAL DRAFT	349.00 • 28.79
_____	SCRIPTOR	295.00 • 24.34
_____	FILMWORKS-SCHEDULING	300.00 • 24.75
_____	FILMWORKS-BUDGETING	300.00 • 24,75
_____	MOVIE MAGIC-SCHEDULING	695.00 • 57.34
_____	MOVIE MAGIC-BUDGETING	595.00 • 49.09

SUBTOTAL: _____

SHIPPING: _____

TOTAL: _____

LONE EAGLE PUBLISHING CO.
2337 Roscomare Rd., #9
Los Angeles, CA 90077
310/471-8066
1/800-345-6257
Fax 310/471-4969

All Prices Subject to Change without Notice.

*Sales Tax applies to California residents only.

College Adoptions 20% OFF

All Payments in US Funds

SHIPPING

DIRECTORIES First/Additional		BOOKS First/Additional
6.00/3.00	USA	4.00/1.50
10.00/5.00	CANADA	5.00/2.00
30.00/25.00	Overseas/Air	15.00/15.
9.00/7.50	Overseas/Surface	5.00/5.

☐ Please send me a catalog

Date: _____

PAYMENT

☐ CHECK ☐ CASH ☐ MONEYORDER CHECK#_____

☐ BILL ☐ VISA ☐ MASTERCARD ☐ AMEX

COMPANY P.O. NUMBER_____

CREDIT CARD NUMBER_____

EXPIRATION DATE_____

CARDHOLDER'S NAME_____

AUTHORIZATION CODE_____

SHIP TO: (*P.O. Boxes not accepted.*)

NAME_____

COMPANY_____

ADDRESS_____

CITY/STATE/ZIP_____

DAYTIME PHONE_____

FOR FAST DELIVERY, FAX IN YOUR ORDER TODAY—310/471-4969

INDEX

ABOUT THE AUTHOR

Ralph Singleton works in the motion picture industry as a Producer, Director and Production Manager. He won an Emmy-award as producer of the critically acclaimed television series, *Cagney & Lacey*. He directed and produced *Stephen King's Graveyard Shift* for Paramount Pictures, executive-produced *Another 48 HRS.* starring Eddie Murphy and Nick Nolte, co-produced Eddie Murphy's directorial debut, *Harlem Nights*, as well as co-produced another Stephen King project for Paramount—*Pet Sematary*. He was head of production for Francis Coppola's Zoetrope Studios and was Production Manager on *Exposed* (MGM/UA), *One From The Heart* (Paramount), *The Winds of War* (USA) (Paramount), *History of the World—Part I* (20th Century Fox), *Somebody Killed Her Husband* (Paramount), *Kojak* (Universal), etc.

Mr. Singleton worked his way up through the Directors Guild first as a Trainee then as an Assistant Director and Production Manager, to finally Director and Producer. His credits are impressive, and he has been honored with awards such as the Women In Film Award, The Nancy Susan Reynolds Award, The Humanitas Prize as well as two Emmy nominations in addition to his Emmy Award for Best Dramatic Series in 1986.

His credits as assistant director include: *Testament* (Paramount), *The Seduction of Joe Tynan* (20th Century Fox), *Greased Lightning* (Warner Bros.), *Taxi Driver* (Columbia), *Network* (Paramount), *The Front* (Warner Bros.), *Three Days of the Condor* (Paramount), *The Gambler* (Paramount).

He is the only assistant director in the history of the Directors Guild of America to work on two Academy Award nominated features in the same year, and be nominated for the prestigious DGA Award for both—*Network* and *Taxi Driver*.

Ralph Singleton is also the author of four highly respected books on film production, FILM SCHEDULING; THE FILM SCHEDULING/FILM BUDGETING WORKBOOK; MOVIE PRODUCTION & BUDGET FORMS... INSTANTLY! and the FILMMAKER'S DICTIONARY. He is currently finishing his fifth book, FILM BUDGETING, which is due in the Spring of 1991. Mr. Singleton also gives seminars on film and television production in the United States for the American Film Institute and in Europe for the Italian-based Forums International.

Mr. Singleton makes his home in Los Angeles, California.